Story Central

Activity Book 5

Viv Lambert, Mo Choy & Suzanne Gaynor

macmillan education

Macmillan Education
4 Crinan Street
London N1 9XW
A division of Macmillan Publishers Limited

Companies and representatives throughout the world

ISBN 978-0-230-45234-3

Written by Viv Lambert ELT Limited, Mo Choy Design Ltd, and Suzanne Gaynor
Additional material written by Tracy Traynor

First published 2015

Designed by Liz Adcock
Page make-up by Carrie Webb (Red Phoenix Design)
Illustrated by Alberto Arzeni (Advocate Art) pp24–25; Pedro Bascon (Advocate Art) pp40–41; Sanjay Charlton (Beehive Illustration) pp16–17; Stevyn Colgan (Beehive Illustration) pp7, 12, 13, 14, 27, 28, 29, 31, 36, 39, 43, 44, 45, 49, 51, 55, 59, 63, 71; Russ Daff (Beehive Illustration) pp78, 79, 81, 82, 83, 85, 86, 87, 88, 89, 91, 93, 95, 102, 103; Dante Ginerva (Advocate Art) pp32–33; Nick Harris (Beehive Illustration) pp9, 18, 20, 26, 35, 36, 42, 47, 52, 58, 68, 76; Roy Knipe (Good Illustration) p48; Fabio Leone (Bright Agency) pp64–65; Mike Love (Bright Agency) p8; Bethan Matthews (Sylvie Poggio Artist Agency) pp6, 15, 22, 30, 38, 47, 54, 60, 62, 70; Paul McCaffrey (Sylvie Poggio Artist Agency) p72; Andrew Painter pp13, 21, 29, 37, 45, 53, 61, 69, 77; Martin Sanders (Beehive Illustration) p73; Victor Tavares (Beehive Illustration) p56; Laszlo Veres (Beehive Illustration) p46; Carrie Webb pp5, 10, 27; Steven Wood (Advocate Art) pp3–77
Cover design by Wild Apple Design Ltd
Cover illustration by Steven Wood (Advocate Art)

Authors' acknowledgements
Thank you to everyone at Macmillan for their support and for allowing us to work in 'our way'.
For patience and tolerance of late-night working, thank you to our families.

Printed and bound in Thailand

2019 2018 2017 2016
10 9 8 7 6 5 4

Contents

Welcome .... page 4

Chapter 1 Then and Now .... page 6

Chapter 2 Work Hard, Play Hard! .... page 14

Chapter 3 Sleep and Dreams .... page 22

Chapter 4 Up and Away! .... page 30

Chapter 5 Real or Imaginary? .... page 38

Chapter 6 On the Ocean Waves .... page 46

Chapter 7 Let's Cook! .... page 54

Chapter 8 Speak Out! .... page 62

Chapter 9 Into the Future .... page 70

Chapter Reviews .... page 78

Grammar Reference .... page 96

Where Have You Been?

1 Complete the questions to ask a friend. Ask, then write about your friend.

What's ....your.......... name?

Where .... live?

Where .... been to?

Where .... go for vacation?

What's .... favorite place?

How .... like to travel?

Where would .... go?

Why?

.... 's World

.... lives in ....

.... 's been to ....

For vacation, ... went to ....

.... 's favorite place is ....

.... likes traveling by ....

.... would like to go to .... because .... likes ....

2 Write about your favorite places.

Where do you like to have fun? ....

What's your favorite trip? ....

What's the most interesting place you've read about in a story?

....

Where do you like to read? ....

Where do you go to meet your friends? ....

Where do you like to go to be alone? ....

3 **Make two verses about you. Circle, then write.**

Last vacation I **went / didn't go** away.
I **went to the beach / read a lot of books** one sunny day.
I really **wanted / didn't want** to stay at home.
Because I **like / don't like** to be alone.

.... is my favorite town.
There are .... and .... all around.
I went to .... with my family.
Then we had .... – I'm so lucky!

4 **Complete with words you know in English.**

The Movies

Outdoor Activities

Space

Celebrations

At the Doctor's

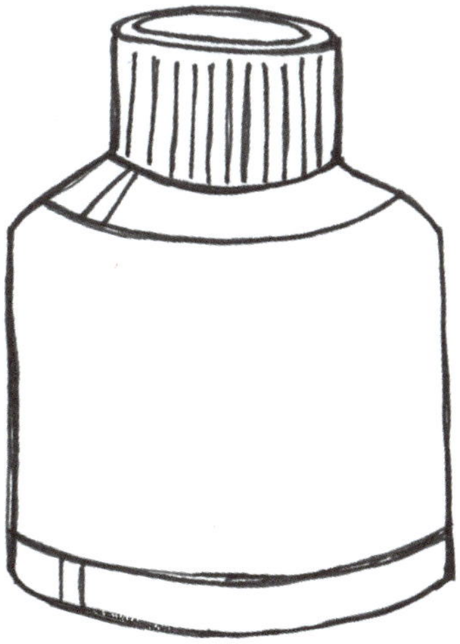

Communication

Chapter 1

Then and Now

Lesson 1

1 Unscramble and write the words. Then find, count, and write the number.

a tolpap ....laptop........ [4]

b hlack .... [ ]

c peolicycedna .... [ ]

d kin nep .... [ ]

e bocharlkda .... [ ]

f luah-hopo .... [ ]

g lebl .... [ ]

h nirodicaty .... [ ]

i trainceveti ....

borwehitad .... [ ]

2 Now circle in the picture the objects in your classroom. Talk to a friend.

There's a laptop.

We don't have any ink pens.

3 Complete with words from Activity 1.

1 If you want to know what a word means, use a ......dictionary...... .

2 When you hear the .... , you can go outside.

3 Don't write in the book with your .... Always use a pencil!

4 You can find the important facts in an ....

5 We watched a DVD of the school trip on the teacher's ....

4 Choose a way to categorize the new words in your notebook.

1 Circle. Then ask and answer.

1 Did / **Were** women go out to work?

2 **Who** / **How** did people communicate?

3 **How** / **What** did they wear?

4 **Why** / **What** was life like for children?

5 **Was** / **Did** they have cars?

2 Complete using the simple past. Then match to the questions in Activity 1.

work ~~write~~ wear have to use

a People didn't have telephones in their homes. They ....wrote.... letters. [2]

b The men went out to work. The women .... at home. [ ]

c There weren't many cars. People .... horses for transportation. [ ]

d When they weren't at school, children .... help at home. [ ]

e Women didn't wear pants. They .... dresses and skirts. [ ]

3 Write information for the website.

Hello, again! I'm going to tell you about life at home 100 years ago.

Children used to ....

People didn't .... They ....

Children ....

Women and girls ....

Who would read this website?

Lesson 3
Telling Stories

1 Cross out the incorrect phrase. Then choose, write, and act out.

your 10th birthday / your first pet / next weekend / your last vacation

Do you remember ....?

Yes, I do. I remember ....…

2 **Read the story in your Student Book. Check (✓) the most important thing in Picture 2.**

1 Zak's bag ☐ 2 the door ☐ 3 the cell phone ☐

3 **Circle.**

1 Mr. Cunningham talks about things **in the past** / **now**.

2 Zak wants to know the time, so he looks **in his bag** / **at the wall**.

3 Zak **likes** / **doesn't like** history.

4 At lunchtime, Zak has to **go outside** / **sit at his desk**.

5 Zak is usually **home** / **on the playground** at lunchtime.

4 **What's behind the door? Think and write.**

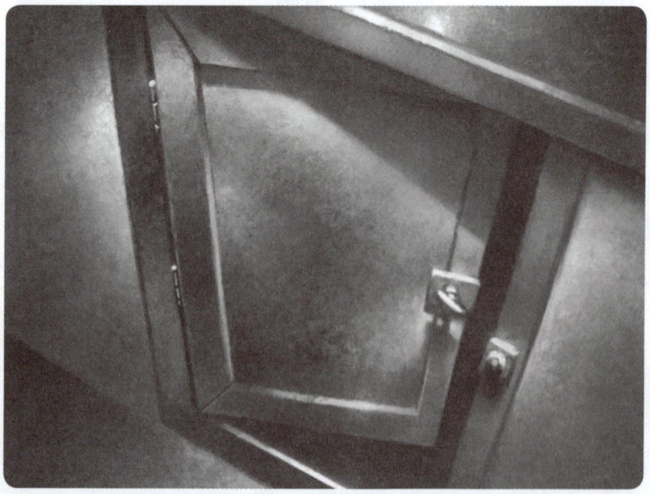

Behind the door, ...

....

....

....

....

1 **How did the characters feel at the start and end of the story? Read and draw arrows.**

Start ←

Zak didn't like history.

Zak thought history was interesting.

Zak thought Mr. Cunningham was boring.

Mr. Cunningham thought Zak was naughty.

Mr. Cunningham thought Zak was nice.

Zak thought Mr. Cunningham was smart.

End

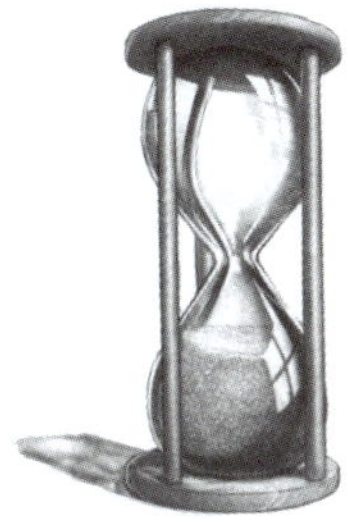

2 **Write P (past) or N (now). Then choose appropriate time expressions to complete the sentences.**

1 In the past ...P...
2 Today ....
3 In 19........ ....
4 Before ....
5 Now ....
6 In the old days ....
7 In 20........ ....
8 These days ....

1 .... girls wore dresses to school.

2 .... many children have cell phones.

3 .... the Aztecs built amazing temples.

4 .... most homes have a computer.

3 **Continue the dialogue between Mr. Cunningham and Zak in your notebook. Use the Story Creator.**

Story Creator

Before, I thought you/history ...
Now, I think ...
It's interesting because ...
These days ...
When I was young, ...
We had/went ...
I used to/didn't use to ...
Did you wear/play ...?
I'm going to study/listen ...

4 **Connect to Me**

Have you ever changed your opinion about someone or something?

Before, I thought ....

Now, I think ....

Lesson 5

1 Complete Yasmin's text.

When I was young, I **1** ✗ didn't use to have an imaginary friend. I **2** ✔ ______ have a pet spider. His name was Arthur. I liked spiders. I liked birds, too. My mom **3** ✔ ______ take me to the park to watch the birds. We **4** ✔ ______ take my favorite peanut butter sandwiches. I **5** ✗ ______ like any other food! I **6** ✔ ______ read a lot of books about animals. I **7** ✗ ______ like sports or watching TV or playing with dolls.

2 Write the questions. Then ask and answer with a friend.

1 use / you / an imaginary friend / Did / to have / ?

Did you use to have an imaginary friend?

2 Did / to jump / use / on your bed / you / ?

______

3 to eat / you / broccoli / use / Did / ?

______

4 trees / to climb / you / Did / use / ?

______

5 use / to do / you / gymnastics / Did / ?

______

Did you use to have an imaginary friend?

No, I didn't.

3 Write about what you *used to* / *didn't use to* do when you were young.

When I was young, I ______ .

I didn't ______ .

I ______ .

I ______ .

1 Complete.

text | chat online | download | earphones | type | ~~video call~~ | records | emails

TO: Uncle Richard

Hi, Uncle Richard

Guess what? Grandpa has a new computer and we had our first **1** video call on Wednesday. He's learning to **2** ______ letters and send **3** ______, too. We can't **4** ______ yet because he can't type very fast. I used to listen to Grandpa's old **5** ______ but now he wants to **6** ______ music! He has **7** ______ so that we can't hear what he listens to. After school, I'm going to teach Grandpa how to **8** ______ on his new cell phone. You'll get a message from him soon!

Alex

2 Write answers for you. Then ask and answer.

1 Can you type quickly? ______.

2 Do you have video calls with friends? ______.

3 Do you download music? ______.

4 Can you text with your eyes closed? ______.

Can you type quickly?

No, I can't. I type very slowly.

Spelling Central

Words with silent letters

3 Circle the words with silent letters. Use the words to complete the puzzle and find the hidden word.

Wednesday guess school after
Grandpa chat video things juice

Hidden word: ______

Lesson 7
CLIL

1 **Read and complete.**

Dear Friend,

Hello from the past! Congratulations! You found our time capsule.

We are from **1** ___Park Side___ School in the **2** ________ . We buried this capsule in **3** 19____ .

We like listening to **4** ________ .
We like reading **5** ________ .
Our favorite food is **6** ________ .
Our favorite sport is **7** ________ .
We hope you enjoyed our letter.
Have a great future!

2 **Use your Student Book research to make an Info Card. Write about what to put in a time capsule.**

Find Out More!

clothes	food	money	movies
TV	music	places	news

3 **Make a time capsule.**

Try it Out

- Fill a big plastic box with things to show how you live.
- Write a letter to the person who will find your time capsule.
- Find a place and bury the time capsule.
- Leave it for someone to find, or you can open it in ten years!

4 **Select and store information on this topic in the Class Info Hub.**

GRAND QUIZ CENTRAL

1 Play with a friend. Choose a character.
2 Write a new question to ask your friend.
3 Take turns asking. Say the answer, then write it in your notebook.
4 If a question is too hard, you can swap! Choose and check (✔) up to three questions. Remember: each swap loses a bonus point!

	Questions to ask Time Traveler	Questions to ask History Maker

1	In the past, what happened if children misbehaved at school?	In the past, why didn't some children go to school?
2	Say and spell. 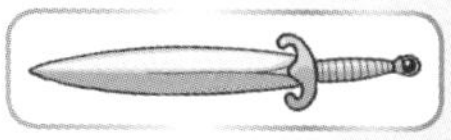	Say and spell. 
3	When Angelo was young, what kind of friend did he use to have?	When Rufus was young, what kind of student did he use to be?
4	What did boys use to wear to school in the old days?	What did girls use to wear to school in the old days?
5	Find the one that doesn't belong: *chalk, pencil, paper, ink pen*	Find the one that doesn't belong: *email, computer, video call, chat online*
6	When will the Westinghouse Time Capsule be opened?	Who wrote a letter in the Westinghouse Time Capsule?
7	In the story, what subject did Mr. Cunningham teach?	In the story, what did Edward lose at school?
8	Did you use to have a favorite toy when you were young?	Did you use to like eating fruit and vegetables when you were young?
9	Unscramble this word: *nldadwoo*	Unscramble this word: *nopreashe*
10	------------------------------------ ?	------------------------------------ ?

Check your friend's answers. Then color your clocks and write your score.

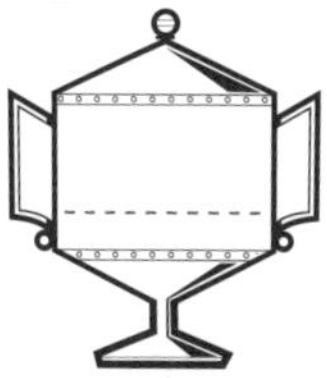

Now choose your title:

- ☐ **Quiz Master!** I understand this topic well.
- ☐ **Quiz Improver!** I don't understand everything.
- ☐ **Quiz Beginner!** I need some help.

Chapter 2 Work Hard, Play Hard!

Lesson 1

1 Write the words.

- baking
- ~~Japanese~~
- photography
- poetry
- karate
- chess

2 Complete with words from Activity 1.

1 Love writing? Use our ......poetry...... app for all your ideas.

2 The best game in the world – but not the easiest! Use our .... app to help you win every time!

3 Cookies or cake? Decide what to make and start .... with this fun app.

4 If you like sports, you'll love this .... app. Learn all the moves!

5 Make your pictures special with this .... app.

6 Learning to speak .... is quick and easy with this app.

3 Choose three apps that you like. Tell a friend.

I like the baking app. I love making cookies.

4 Choose a way to categorize the new words in your notebook.

Lesson 2

1 What else did Peter say? Unscramble and write.

1 lived / in my house / three years / I've / for / .
I've lived in my house for three years.

2 I / I've / was / learned / since / five / . / Japanese
....

3 years / for / my / I've / two / best / known / . / friend
....

4 school / since / at / year / We've / karate / done / last / .
....

5 three / has / for / worked / mom / My / here / . /years /
....

2 Complete the questions. Then ask and answer.

1 How long you/live have you lived in your house?
2 How long you/know .... your best friend?
3 How long you/study .... English?
4 How long you/have .... your school bag?

3 Look and complete the magazine article. Use the present perfect and *for* or *since*.

Hobby News

Hannah Bakes the World's Best Cakes!

Hannah is 11 years old but she 's done
a lot .... she started baking!
Hannah .... cakes with her dad
.... she was in elementary school.
She .... in competitions
.... several years.
She ....
....

Where would you read this type of article?

Lesson 3
Telling Stories

1 **Cross out the incorrect phrase. Then choose, write, and act out.**

tomorrow / for a week / for ages / since this morning

I haven't seen you ______________ !

I've been ______________ . I've ______________ since ______________ ...

2 **Read the story in your Student Book. Circle the words that describe Andy. Then check (✓) the sentence that describes the story.**

busy hard-working stupid smart relaxed

1 It has clues and puzzles. ☐
2 It uses animal characters to teach us about life. ☐
3 It's about a dark and scary place. ☐

3 **Write answers.**

1 Is Grant happy with his life? Yes, he is.
2 Does Andy think Grant is smart? ______________
3 Why doesn't Grant collect food for the winter? ______________
4 Where does Andy put the food? ______________
5 When is Andy going to relax? ______________

4 **Imagine Andy at home in the winter. Check (✓) the correct descriptions.**

At home in the winter, Andy ...

is warm	☐	is cold	☐		
is alone	☐	is hungry	☐	is with his family	☐
relaxes	☐	works	☐	has a lot to eat	☐

Lesson 4
Time to Think

1 **Change what happened in the story. Make notes.**

Andy shut the door. ....

Andy didn't help Grant. ....

Grant felt stupid. ....

Grant lost a friend. ....

2 **Choose and complete. Use a time expression and *for* or *since*.**

Writing Tools

last summer | three years | a long time | ~~last month~~
2010 | two months | he was five | six weeks

1 Andy has been in the field since last month.
2 Grant has played music ....
3 Andy hasn't seen Grant ....
4 Andy has lived in his house ....
5 Grant has played in the Sun ....

3 **Write a different ending for the story in your notebook. Use the Story Creator.**

Story Creator

Come in and sit/eat ...
Please help ...
Why don't you ...?
You're/I'm so cold/hungry ...
When/Why did you ...?

How long have you been ...?
Thank you for ...
I've/You've been stupid/nice ...
Next summer, I'm going to ...

4 **Connect to Me**

Have you ever played when you should have studied? How did you feel?

I .... but I should have ....

I felt ....

1 Complete Scarlett's old diary entry.

might study
's going to bring
'm not going to take
~~is going to talk~~
might stay
's going to show

Tomorrow, a famous artist **1** is going to talk to us. He **2** .... his paintings into the class so that we can see them. After lunch, he **3** .... us how to draw animals because they're very difficult. I haven't decided yet, but I **4** .... art at college after school. Rufus doesn't know if he wants to go to the talk or not. He says he **5** .... home because he doesn't like art very much. We have to take a picture to show the artist, but I **6** .... this picture of Hamish – it's awful!

2 Now circle the definite plans and underline the possible actions in the diary.

3 Write the questions. Then ask and answer with a friend.

1 What / you / do / this evening? What are you going to do this evening?
2 you / watch / a movie? Are you going to watch a movie?
3 you / go / to the park? ....
4 you / chat online / with your friends? ....
5 What / you / get / for your birthday? ....

What are you going to do this evening?

I might go to my friend's house. What about you?

I'm going to bake a cake.

4 Write about what you're going to do and might do this evening.

After school, I'm going to ....
I might not ....
After that, I ....

1 Unscramble and write.

Love school, love learning – our message to all new students.

We know that school life is full of 1 hsgelcalen challenges . There are so many 2 sstte .... to 3 saps .... – you might worry that you're going to 4 lifa .... At Park Side School, we want every student to 5 cedsuce .... School is more than just good 6 sgared .... It should be fun with friendly 7 copttosmeiin .... where every student can 8 eakt rpta .... You might not take home a 9 etfctcriiae .... or a 10 prtohy .... but doing things that you really like doing is the best way to prepare for 11 gelleco ....

2 Do the survey. Ask and answer, then write sentences about your friend.

	Me	Friend
1 I want to succeed at school.	✔	
2 I like challenges.		
3 I often get good grades.		
4 I've gotten a lot of certificates.		
5 I always fail my math test.		

Do you want to succeed at school?

Yes, I do.

....

....

....

Spelling Central

Words with *ll*

3 Write words with *ll*.

A		B
sma	ll	ed
pu		er
rea		y
fa		ing

from A + *ll*	from A + *ll* + from B
small	....
....	....
....	....
	....
	....

Lesson 7 CLIL

~~succeed~~	might
website	take part
certificate	going to

1 Read and complete.

Pick Up Trash Day

We've helped a village in Nicaragua get clean water. It's changed their lives. Now we need money for more projects like this – and we need YOUR help to 1 succeed.
2 ______ in Pick Up Trash Day on July 15th. For every street we clean, we make $5 for Nicaragua.
It 3 ______ be hard work, but it's 4 ______ be fun, too!
Everyone who takes part gets a 5 ______.

Go to our 6 ______ for more information or to give money.

2 Use your Student Book research to make an Info Card. Write about what your community needs.

Find Out More!

children schools trees food sports water

3 Do a project to help your community.

Try it Out

- Choose a project or decide on a challenge to make money.
- Make posters and ask friends and family to take part.
- Do the challenge. Make it fun for everyone.
- After, thank everyone who helped you and tell them what you succeeded in doing. Give them certificates!

4 Select and store information on this topic in the Class Info Hub.

GRAND QUIZ CENTRAL

1 Play with a friend. Choose a character.
2 Write a new question to ask your friend.
3 Take turns asking. Say the answer, then write it in your notebook.
4 If a question is too hard, you can swap! Choose and check (✔) up to three questions. Remember: each swap loses a bonus point!

	Questions to ask Active Ant	Questions to ask Busy Bee

1	Say something you might do tonight.	Say something you're going to do tomorrow.
2	Give an example of a word with *ll* in the middle.	Give an example of a word with *ll* at the end.
3	Complete: *I don't want to go to the party. I .... stay at home.*	Complete: *I .... go shopping tomorrow. I'm not sure yet.*
4	In the story, who's written a song?	In the story, who bakes a corn cake?
5	What's Angelo going to do to get into music school?	What might Yasmin do right after school?
6	Find the one that doesn't belong: *trophy, pass, certificate, grades*	Find the one that doesn't belong: *competition, test, challenge, succeed*
7	Choose: *On an expedition, you might help build a school / do judo.*	Choose: *On an expedition you might work hard / have a vacation.*
8	Complete: *I've been at this school .... five years.*	Complete: *He's learned English .... 2010.*
9	Unscramble this word: *opryet*	Unscramble this word: *otaphgohrpy*
10	..............................?	..............................?

Check your friend's answers. Then color your flowers and write your score.

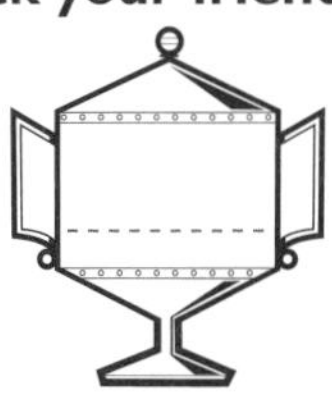

Now choose your title:

- **Quiz Master!** I understand this topic well.
- **Quiz Improver!** I don't understand everything.
- **Quiz Beginner!** I need some help.

Chapter 3 Sleep and Dreams

Lesson 1

1 Write the words.

frightening disappointing awful ~~amazing~~ realistic confusing weird embarrassing

amazing

....

....

....

....

....

....

....

2 Complete. Use words from Activity 1.

1 It was .... that we were too late to see the movie.

2 This story is .... I can't understand it at all.

3 The movie was .... – we really didn't like it.

4 Everyone laughed when I dropped my cake! It was ....

3 Talk to a friend. Say sentences using the words in Activity 1.

> Last night, I had an *amazing* pizza at a restaurant.

4 Choose a way to categorize the new words in your notebook.

1 Circle to make the second sentence mean the same as the first.

1 The movie is worse than the book.

The movie **isn't as good as / is just as good as** the book.

2 The photo is better than the painting.

The painting **is just as good as / isn't as good as** the photo.

3 Your story is more realistic than my story.

My story **is just as realistic as / isn't as realistic as** your story.

4 Will's dream wasn't as frightening as Emma's dream.

Emma's dream **was more frightening than / was just as frightening as** Will's dream.

2 Complete the sentences for you. Tell a friend. Do you agree?

1 Adventure stories ....aren't as interesting as........ horror stories.

2 Baking cookies .... photography.

3 A carousel .... a roller coaster.

4 Learning Japanese .... learning English.

5 My hair.. your hair.

3 Choose two books. Write a review for the book review website and color the stars. Remember to add your name, age and country.

☆☆☆☆☆ ☆☆☆☆☆

My Review of .... **and** ....

I think that .... is ....

The plot in .... is ....

the plot in ....

The .... in .... isn't ....

the ending in ....

Lesson 3
Telling Stories

1 **Write another correct word. Then choose, write, and act out.**

weird / confusing / frightening / ....

Have you ever dreamed about .... ?

Yes, I have. / No, I haven't. I sometimes dream about ....
It's ....

2 **Read the story in your Student Book. Check (✓) the sentence that describes the story. Then circle the story type.**

1 Strange and magical things happen in the story. ☐

2 The story is about things that happen in real life. ☐

3 The story is about things that happened in history. ☐

historical fiction   fantasy   realistic fiction

3 **Write *true* or *false*.**

1 Alice is enjoying listening to the story. ......false......

2 She sees a white rabbit asleep on the grass. ....

3 Alice often sees white rabbits. ....

4 Alice falls down the rabbit hole. ....

5 The story takes place a long time ago. ....

4 **Where's the rabbit going? What's he going to do? Think and write.**

....

....

....

....

....

Lesson 4
Time to Think

1 Read and draw an arrow to the correct person for each thought.

This is a weird place.

Where's my fan?

Who's she?

How frightening: a giant!

This is so disappointing.

What big ears!

2 Complete. Then circle the time expressions.

~~To my surprise~~	Soon	Fortunately	Finally	Unfortunately

1 To my surprise , a giant rabbit jumped out of a hole.

2 .... , I found the key and could open the door.

3 .... , I was bigger than the door and couldn't go into the garden.

4 .... it's going to get dark.

5 .... , I went to bed and fell asleep.

3 Imagine that you went to Wonderland. Write about your adventure in your notebook. Use the Story Creator.

Story Creator

One night, I went to Wonderland.

To my surprise, there was a/ were a lot of ...

Fortunately, I met/spoke to ...

He/She was very ...

Unfortunately, I ate/drank a ...

When I saw ..., I was very frightened/excited.

It was amazing/disappointing ...

4 Connect to Me

Have you ever had a bad dream that you thought was very realistic?

I dreamed ....

....

Lesson 5

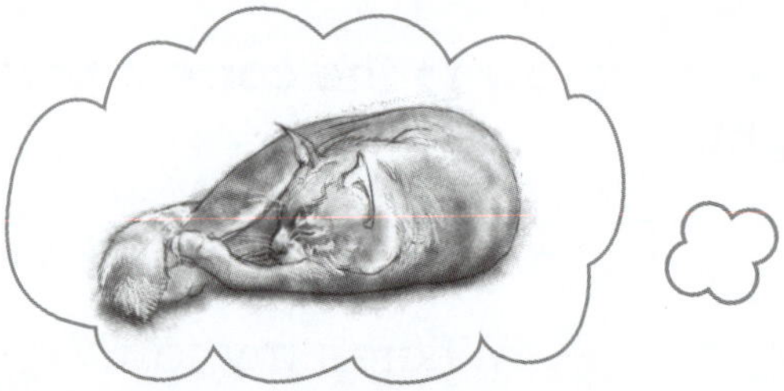

1 Circle.

I just read an 1 **interested / interesting** article about animals and sleeping. Do you know that cats can sleep for about 12 hours every day? When they're 2 **boring / bored**, they just fall asleep. Giraffes are completely different. They only sleep for a few minutes and they sleep with their eyes open. I think that's 3 **frightening / frightened**, don't you? When we're on the school bus, Angelo always sleeps with his mouth open. I'm always very 4 **embarrassed / embarrassing** when I'm sitting next to him.

2 **Complete with *ing* or *ed*.**

1 I'm frighten*ed*...... if I have to sleep in the dark.

2 It's disappoint.......... when a friend forgets your birthday.

3 It's embarrass.......... when I can't pronounce a word.

4 I'm interest.......... when the teacher tells us funny stories.

5 It's bor.......... when there aren't any good shows on TV.

3 **Write about how you feel. Then talk to a friend.**

1 If I have nothing to do, I ....

2 It's embarrassing when ....

3 It's .... when my friends don't call me.

4 Watching a horror movie before bed ....

5 When ....

1 Complete.

fall asleep | stay awake | pillow | the dark | stay up | ~~lie down~~

You're tired. It's time to **1** lie down, turn off the light, and relax your head on a comfortable **2** ________. But what happens if you're an astronaut? In space, it's hard to sleep. There's no difference between night and day and astronauts often **3** ________ for a long time. But it's good if you're scared of **4** ________ because the sun comes up every 90 minutes in space! It would be exciting to **5** ________ late and watch the stars through the window. When astronauts finally **6** ________, they dream about discovering new planets.

2 **Write answers for you. Then ask and answer.**

1 Do you like to stay up late? ________.

2 Do you fall asleep easily? ________.

3 How many pillows do you use? ________.

4 Are you frightened of the dark? ________.

5 Do you always lie down to sleep? ________.

Do you like to stay up late?

No, I don't because I don't like being tired at school.

Spelling Central

Words with *gh*

3 **Find and circle six words with *gh* missing. Then write them out correctly.**

right

____

____

____

____

____

Lesson 7

CLIL

1 Read and write *true* or *false*.

Light and Sleep

Light makes you stay awake in the day. Before we had electricity, people went to bed when it got dark and got up at sunrise. Lights in our homes have changed our body clocks. We now have more light at night time and so people stay up later and sleep less than in the past. Don't forget that your TV and computer screens give light, too. So turn them off! When you use them just before bedtime, you don't fall asleep as quickly as you should – and you don't sleep as well.

1 Electricity has changed how long we sleep. ____true____

2 People go to bed earlier now than in the past. ____________

3 People used to sleep more in the past. ____________

4 You sleep better when you watch TV before going to bed. ____________

5 You shouldn't use your computer late at night. ____________

2 **Use your Student Book research to make an Info Card. Write about body clocks and sleep cycles.**

Find Out More!

When should you sleep? What changes your body clock?
What happens to you when you sleep? What helps you sleep?

3 **Write some advice about good sleep habits. Then try it out.**

Try it Out

- Read the quiz again for information.
- In groups, write six tips about good sleep habits.
- Take your own advice! Follow the tips for two weeks.
- After two weeks, take the quiz again. Did you get more As? Have the tips worked? Tell the class.

4 **Select and store information on this topic in the Class Info Hub.**

GRAND QUIZ CENTRAL

1 Play with a friend. Choose a character.
2 Write a new question to ask your friend.
3 Take turns asking. Say the answer, then write it in your notebook.
4 If a question is too hard, you can swap! Choose and check (✔) up to three questions. Remember: each swap loses a bonus point!

	Questions to ask Daydreamer	Questions to ask Sleepyhead
1	What were the words on the bottle in Alice's dream in the story?	What does Alice eat in her dream in the story?
2	Spell this phrase. 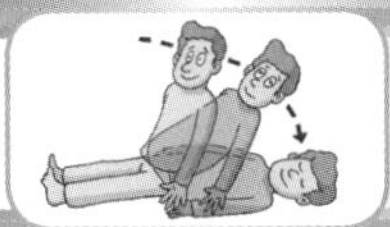	Spell this word. 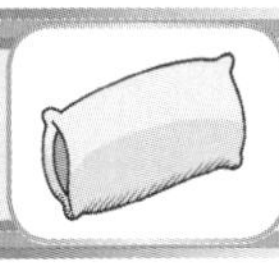
3	Is a hamster smaller than a rabbit?	Is a turtle as big as a whale?
4	Should you exercise at night or in the day?	Should you get up at the same time every day or later on weekends?
5	Say in a different way: *Tigers are more frightening than sharks.*	Say in a different way: *The movie wasn't as exciting as the book.*
6	Angelo dreamed about a monster. How did he feel?	Yasmin dreamed about flying. How was her dream?
7	When did you feel disappointed? Why?	When did you feel you embarrassed? Why?
8	Give an example of a *gh* word.	Give an example of a *gh* word.
9	Unscramble this description: *nmaaizg*	Unscramble this description: *ogusnfinc*
10	………………………………………………?	………………………………………………?

Check your friend's answers. Then color your dream bubbles and write your score.

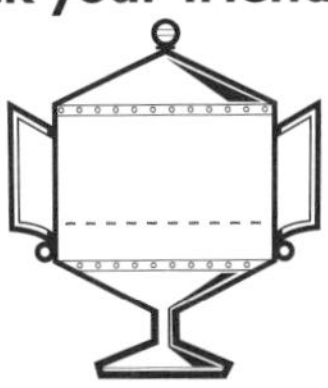

Now choose your title:

- ☐ **Quiz Master!** I understand this topic well.
- ☐ **Quiz Improver!** I don't understand everything.
- ☐ **Quiz Beginner!** I need some help.

Chapter 4 Up and Away!

Lesson 1

1 Look and circle.

In the sky, there's a big 1 **balloon** / **basket** with a star on it. On the left, another balloon is 2 **landing** / **taking off**. A boy is standing in the 3 **ropes** / **basket**. He's looking at the 4 **flight** / **view** of the mountains. One of the 5 **passengers** / **ropes** is a dog. A man is pulling the 6 **passengers** / **ropes** – it looks difficult. Look at the balloon on the right. There isn't much 7 **hot air** / **view** in it.

2 Unscramble and write.

Ladies and gentlemen, this is your pilot speaking. I'd like to welcome you on 1 tfhilg .... 46DB1 to Buenos Aires. We are preparing to 2 keat ffo .... in ten minutes. Please put your bags in a 3 efas .... place under your seat or above your head. Now sit back and relax and I'll speak to you again before we 4 ndal ....

3 Choose words from Activities 1 and 2. Tell a friend what they mean.

Passengers – they're the people who are traveling.

4 Choose a way to categorize the new words in your notebook.

Lesson 2

1 **Read the trip itinerary. Complete the sentences.**

Monday
Fly to Houston, Texas.

Tuesday
2:00 p.m. watch a baseball game
6:00 p.m. eat at The Nacho Café

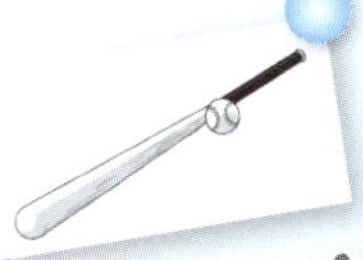

Wednesday
9:00 a.m. see the animals at Houston Zoo

Thursday
11:00 a.m. visit the Johnson Space Center

Friday
10:30 a.m. go to hot air balloon show
7:00 p.m. watch a movie

Saturday
....
....
....

Sunday
....
....
....

On Monday, **1** I 'm flying .... to Houston. On Tuesday, we **2** .... a baseball game and then we **3** .... at The Nacho Café. On Wednesday, **4** I .... the animals at Houston Zoo. On Thursday, I **5** .... the Johnson Space Center. On Friday, we **6** .... to a hot air balloon show and in the evening I **7** .... a movie!

2 **Look at your itinerary. Write questions. Then ask and answer.**

1 When / you / go to the zoo? When are you going to the zoo?
2 you / fly home / on Friday? Are you flying home on Friday?
3 What / you / do / on Thursday? ....
4 Where / you / eat / on Tuesday? ....
5 you / watch / a baseball game? ....

3 **Now complete the itinerary for Saturday and Sunday. Then write.**

On Saturday morning, I'm .... with my friends.
On Saturday evening I'm not .... I'm ....
On Sunday afternoon my friends and I ....
On Sunday evening I ....

What type of information is in an itinerary?

Lesson 3
Telling Stories

1 **Cross out the incorrect phrase. Then choose, write, and act out.**

last Saturday / for your birthday / after school / tomorrow

What are you doing .... ?

I'm ....

2 **Read the story in your Student Book. Check (✓) the sentence that describes the story. Then circle the story type.**

1 The story is about how people used to live every day in the past. ☐

2 Everything in the story is true. ☐

3 Dangerous and exciting things happen. ☐

factual/non-fiction   science fiction   adventure

3 **Write *true* or *false*.**

1 The doctor is flying the balloon. ......true......

2 The birds aren't dangerous. ....

3 Hot air should make the balloon go up. ....

4 The birds make a hole in the balloon. ....

5 The men throw out the food because they aren't hungry. ....

4 **Where do Richard and the doctor fly to next? Think and write.**

....

....

....

....

....

Lesson 4
Time to Think

1 **What was Joe thinking? Make notes.**

When this happened, ...

Joe was thinking ...

I'm cold and frightened.

2 **Unscramble and write.**

1 I / . / balloon / the / Later, / repaired

----

2 looking / Richard / worried / Meanwhile, / . / was / very

----

3 there / everywhere / crocodiles / were / . / Suddenly,

----

4 month / we / again / arrived / One / home / later, / .

----

3 **Imagine you're Joe and you went on another adventure. Write about it in your notebook. Use the Story Creator.**

Story Creator

We went to ...

I knew that it was dangerous/difficult ...

Later, I found/swam ...

Meanwhile, a ...

The next morning, I saw ...

When I looked/shouted ...

I felt tired/safe ...

... looked angry/excited.

4 **Connect to Me**

Have you ever done something difficult to help a friend?

I -- .

Lesson 5

1 Circle. Then ask and answer.

1 Do you find **nothing** / **everything** you need on the internet?

2 Do you think that **everyone** / **everything** uses the internet for homework?

3 Are you reading **nothing** / **anything** exciting now?

4 Would you like to do **everything** / **something** this weekend?

5 Do you know **anyone** / **no one** who's learning Japanese?

> Do you find everything you need on the internet?

> No. Sometimes it's difficult to find information.

2 Complete.

no one | anything | someone | ~~everything~~ | anyone | nothing | something

Daniel: This encyclopedia's great. It has **1** everything you need to know about flying.

Angelo: You're right, but you could also look on the internet. There's always **2** .... interesting there.

Daniel: Sometimes I look for ages on the internet and I don't find **3** ....

Angelo: I know **4** .... who finds jokes on the internet. They're awful! **5** .... thinks they're funny.

Yasmin: I don't know **6** .... who uses an encyclopedia now … except you, Daniel.

Daniel: There's **7** .... wrong with that, Yasmin!

3 Write about your plans for this evening. Use words from Activities 1 and 2.

I'm doing .... very special this evening.

I'm meeting ....

I don't know ....

Lesson 6

1 Complete the words with the correct vowels.

We traveled by **1** tr_a_ _i_n from **2** N__rth __ m__r__c__ to **3** S__ __th __m__r__c__ and then by **4** sh__p to **5** __fr__c__. A month later we arrived in **6** __ __r__p__. Grandma wanted to climb mountains so we bought a map and a compass. I left my **7** p__ssp__rt and my sunglasses in the bookshop!

Our next journey was to **8** __s__ __, where we rode on elephants. Now we're at a beach café in **9** __ __str__l__ __. Soon, we're traveling by **10** __ __rpl__n__ to **11** __nt__rct__c__. We have a new **12** b__ckp__ck because we need lots of snow clothes.

2 Write answers. Then ask and answer.

1 What continents have you visited? ....

2 Which continent would you like to visit? ....

3 What's your favorite way to travel? ....

4 What's important to take with you when you visit another country? ....

What continents have you visited?

I've visited North America and Europe.

Spelling Central

Compound nouns

3 Find, circle, and match the nouns to make compound words. Then write the words: one word or two?

....

....

Lesson 7
CLIL

1 Read and circle.

BE CAREFUL! TURTLES CROSSING!

Some animals use the sun, moon, and stars as clues to find which way to go. Baby turtles don't have 1 **maps** / **watches** to get to the 2 **town** / **ocean**! They use the light from the moon. And they need to get to the water as quickly as they can. Lights from houses and cars can 3 **help** / **confuse** them. They go the wrong way and sometimes try to cross roads, which is very dangerous. But 4 **everyone** / **no one** can help. When there are baby turtles, please turn 5 **on** / **off** your lights! Don't use 6 **flashlights** / **computers** or 7 **light fires** / **play music** on the beach at night. Then the turtles will get to the water safely.

2 **Use your Student Book research to make an Info Card. Write about migrating animals.**

Find Out More!

Why? When? How far? Where to? Which way/direction?

3 **Make and use a compass.**

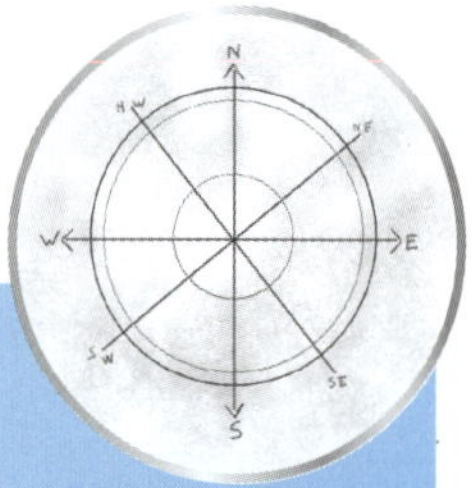

Try it Out

- Face the front of the classroom. Write FRONT at the top of your paper and draw a big circle.
- Draw arrows and write labels: E (where the sun rises), W (where the sun goes down), N, and S.
- Mark the points between the four main compass points: **NE** northeast **SE** southeast **SW** southwest **NW** northwest.
- Use your compass to play a game with a friend.

4 **Select and store information on this topic in the Class Info Hub.**

GRAND QUIZ CENTRAL

1 Play with a friend. Choose a character.
2 Write a new question to ask your friend.
3 Take turns asking. Say the answer, then write it in your notebook.
4 If a question is too hard, you can swap! Choose and check (✔) up to three questions. Remember: each swap loses a bonus point!

Questions to ask Adventure Monkey

Questions to ask World Traveler

	Questions to ask Adventure Monkey	Questions to ask World Traveler
1	What do you use to tie a balloon to the ground?	What's the word for the people traveling in the balloon?
2	Make a compound noun: *back…*	Make a compound noun: *white…*
3	What are you doing in your next class?	How are you traveling home after school?
4	In the story, why can't Joe go on the balloon adventure?	In the story, what are Richard and the doctor going to Africa to find?
5	How does Angelo know about hot air balloons?	Who at Story Central has traveled in a hot air balloon?
6	What light do baby turtles follow to find their way to the ocean?	Where do adult turtles go after they bury their eggs in the sand?
7	Which continent is southeast of Asia?	Which continent is northwest of Africa?
8	Complete: *Are you … basketball tonight?*	Complete: *What are you … this weekend?*
9	What's the opposite of *everyone*?	What's the opposite of *everything*?
10	______________________?	______________________?

Check your friend's answers. Then color your stickers and write your score.

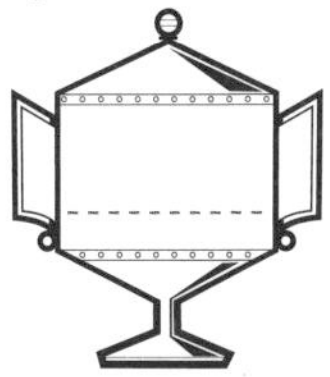

Now choose your title:

- ☐ **Quiz Master!** I understand this topic well.
- ☐ **Quiz Improver!** I don't understand everything.
- ☐ **Quiz Beginner!** I need some help.

Chapter 5 Real or Imaginary?

Lesson 1

1 **Unscramble and write the words. Then look and number.**

1 a cool onctot ....cotton.... T-shirt

2 some odow .... for the fire

3 a liks .... tie for Grandpa

4 some eterhal .... boots

5 some lowo .... for a new scarf

6 a lsictap .... ruler for school

7 a vrlise .... clock for Mom's birthday

8 a slasg .... lamp for my bedroom

2 **Write *true* or *false*.**

1 You can see your face in a silver cup. ....true....

2 Wood isn't natural – people make it. ....

3 Plastic is always hard. ....

4 Glass usually breaks when it hits something. ....

5 Wool is warmer than cotton. ....

3 **Look for things in your classroom. Tell a friend.**

Your watch is silver.

There isn't any wood.

4 **Choose a way to categorize the new words in your notebook.**

Lesson 2

1 Match.

1 What's the box used for? — b

2 What are your gloves made of?

3 What's your bag made of?

4 What's that plate used for?

5 What are the bottles used for?

a It's made of silk.

b It's used for my ink pens.

c They're used for water or juice.

d They're made of wool.

e It's used for cake.

2 Complete. Then choose another item and tell a friend about it.

1 What _'s_ the robot _made of_? It _'s made of_ wood.

2 What _'s_ this bag _used for_? It _'s used for_ shopping.

3 What ________ the boots ________? They ________ leather.

4 What ________ the cap ________? It ________ sports.

5 What ________ that pen ________? It ________ coloring.

6 What ________ your sunglasses ________? They're ________ plastic.

3 Choose an item from the shopping website. Write a description with *made of* and *used for*.

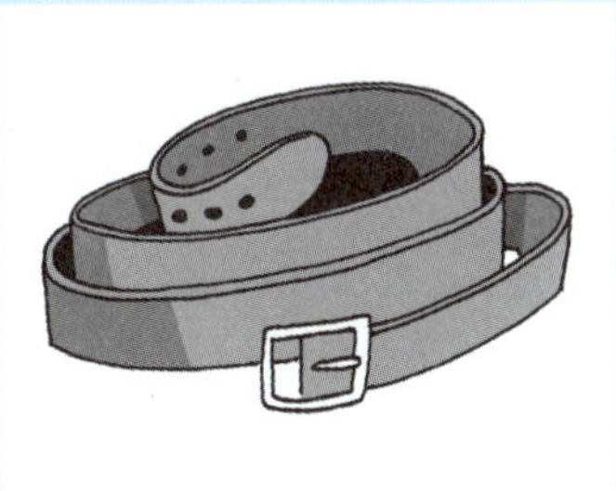

____

Condition: ________

Description: This ________ is made of ________.

It's ________ and ________.

It's ________.

Price: $ ________

What kind of information should your description have?

Lesson 3
Telling Stories

1 Write another correct word. Then choose, write, and act out.

dress / cake / birthday card / necklace / ....

That .... *looks great!*

Thanks.

Did you make it?

No, I didn't. ....

2 Read the story in your Student Book. Write F (fantasy) or P (poem).

1 It tells you about what happened in a dream. ☐

2 You can read it with rhythm. ☐

3 There are rhyming words at the end of lines. ☐

4 It has weird creatures like a giant fish made of jell-o. ☐

3 Circle.

1 The boy is **awake** / **asleep** now.

2 His boat is made of **food** / **things you can't eat**.

3 The queen's castle is **very cold** / **really warm**.

4 The queen **is nice to** / **doesn't like** the boy.

5 In the strange land, **everything is** / **most things are** good to eat.

4 Who or what is the boy going to meet on his journey? Think and write.

....

....

1 **What are good and bad things in the strange land? Make notes.**

2 **Number the adjectives in order. Then match to a noun.**

Writing Tools

a She was a	2	young	1	beautiful	boat.
b This is my		green		small	bird.
c She wore a		gold		new	crown.
d In the sky was a		white		paper	monster.
e Suddenly I saw a		big		yellow	queen.

3 **Imagine the queen's diary entry for that day. Write it in your notebook. Use the Story Creator.**

Story Creator

The boy sailed/visited ...
He looked excited/nice ...
I don't know where/what he ...
My strange land is ...
It's an amazing/frightening ...
There are a lot of ...
The ocean is full of ...
I feel worried/happy about ...
I hope he doesn't ...

4 **Connect to Me**

Do you always do what people tell you to do? Why?/Why not?

.... because ....

....

Lesson 5

1 **Complete with the passive.**

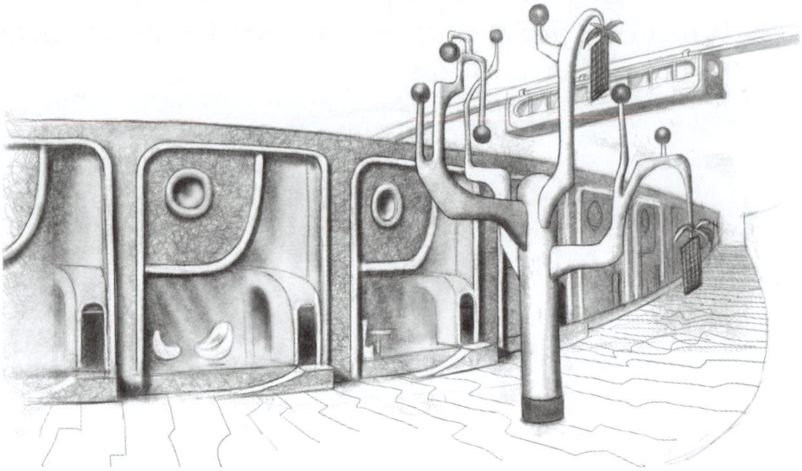

Do you like my painting of an imaginary land? All the houses **1** make are made of wood and glass. They're bright because they **2** paint ______ in different colors. There aren't any cars or buses on the street but special trains **3** use ______ to take children to school. Interesting food **4** eat ______ in this land. The chocolate is delicious and it **5** grow ______ on magic trees. You can talk to everyone because only one language **6** speak ______, but it isn't English!

2 **Unscramble and write. Then talk with a friend.**

1 yellow / bedroom / . / is / painted / My

My bedroom is painted yellow.

2 in my family / languages / are / Two / spoken / .

______

3 . / on Sundays / In my house, / only eaten / is / cake

______

4 grown / Vegetables / in my garden / . / are

______

5 is / or dad / . / by my mom / always made / Lunch

______

My bedroom is painted blue.

Nice! My bedroom is painted yellow.

3 **Write about an imaginary land.**

In my imaginary land, the houses are ______.

______ are found ______.

The food is ______.

______ is spoken ______.

1 Complete.

Pasta and pesto. Hot or cold, it's delicious – but how is it made? We found out!

You need: a basil plant, garlic, nuts, olive oil, and cheese. First, the best green leaves are **1** pick ...picked... from the plant. The brown leaves are **2** remove .... The nuts are washed and then they're **3** grind .... Next, the olive oil, basil leaves, garlic, and nuts are **4** mix .... into a paste. Finally, the cheese is added. The paste is put into jars and they're **5** deliver .... to the stores.

2 **Write answers. Then talk to a friend. Do you have the same ideas?**

1 Name two things that can be roasted. ....

2 How is something dried? ....

3 What's the opposite of *opened*? ....

4 Name two things that can be ground. ....

5 Where's wood collected from? ....

Name two things that can be roasted.

Meat and cocoa beans.

Spelling Central

Past participles

3 **How is the past participle formed? Write the verbs in the correct group. Then write more examples for each group. Who can find most?**

close
~~carry~~
find
play

change y to ied	+ ed	+ d	irregular
carried			

Lesson 7
CLIL

1 Read and circle.

Chalk

Chalk is a type of 1 **plastic / rock** that is 2 **made / washed** under the ocean. This is too hard to draw with, so it's made into chalk sticks for artists.

The chalk rock is 3 **ground / picked** into a powder. The chalk powder is 4 **roasted / mixed** with water and a color pigment to make a 5 **paste / pencil**. Then the paste is made into thin stick shapes and 6 **dried / cooled** in an oven.

Oil is sometimes added to artists' chalk to make it softer. And more pigment is added, so the color is darker than chalk that's used for writing on 7 **paper / blackboards**.

2 Use your Student Book research to make an Info Card. Write about how things are made.

Find Out More!

Is it grown or made?
What happens to it?
What's the product at the end?

3 Make a flow chart to show how something is made.

Try it Out

- Choose a process, e.g. how paint is made.
- Decide on the number of steps to show.
- Write a sentence for each step and draw a picture.
- Draw arrows between steps so that the order is clear.

4 Select and store information on this topic in the Class Info Hub.

GRAND QUIZ CENTRAL

1 Play with a friend. Choose a character.
2 Write a new question to ask your friend.
3 Take turns asking. Say the answer, then write it in your notebook.
4 If a question is too hard, you can swap! Choose and check (✔) up to three questions. Remember: each swap loses a bonus point!

	Questions to ask Jell-o Monster 	Questions to ask Chocolate Giant 
1	What are fries made of?	What are newspapers made of?
2	Spell this material. 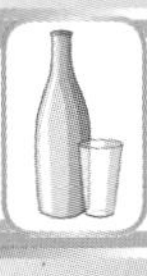	Spell this material. 
3	What are cookies used for in the strange land of the story?	What's lettuce used for in the strange land of the story?
4	Complete using the passive: *They speak English. English is ...*	Complete using the passive: *They write letters. Letters are ...*
5	What did Yasmin say about Africa? *Penguins …*	What did Yasmin say about Australia? *Kangaroos …*
6	What are your shoes made of?	What is your pencil case made of?
7	Complete: *Cocoa pods are (pick) … from trees.*	Complete: *Science is (study) … at my school.*
8	What food is used for making tempera paint?	Name one thing paint pigments are made of.
9	Find the one that doesn't belong: *paste, remove, collect, deliver*	Find the one that doesn't belong: *wool, cotton, silver, silk*
10	-- ?	-- ?

Check your friend's answers. Then color your jewels and write your score.

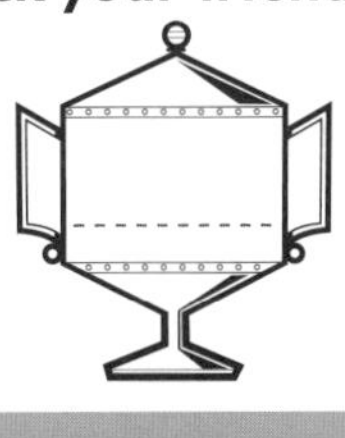

Now choose your title:

- ☐ **Quiz Master!** I understand this topic well.
- ☐ **Quiz Improver!** I don't understand everything.
- ☐ **Quiz Beginner!** I need some help.

Chapter 6 On the Ocean Waves

Lesson 1

1 **Write the words.**

crew
lifeboat
survivor
life jacket
~~rock~~

2 **Unscramble and write.**

It's *Adventure at Sea* – the online game where you have to escape from the **1** ksninig ......sinking...... ship. You and the **2** wcer .... start on the ship. You have to get to a **3** foblaeit .... A man's in the water. He's swimming for the **4** okcr ...., but there are sharks! Can someone **5** ercseu .... him before the sharks get him? You want to try, but you might **6** drnow .... because you can't swim. You can choose two people to **7** veas .... , but what's going to happen to the others?

3 **Tell a friend things you might do in the game.**

You might swim without a life jacket.

You might look for another lifeboat.

4 **Choose a way to categorize the new words in your notebook.**

1 Circle.

A lucky dog!

He has his life jacket on now, but Buddy 1 wasn't wearing / didn't wear it yesterday when he 2 landed / was landing in the lake. Buddy has lived next to the lake with Mr. and Mrs. Marley for ten years. Last night, he 3 waited / was waiting for Mr. Marley to come home when he 4 heard / was hearing the sound of a car. Buddy ran outside. The car 5 was coming / came around the corner when Buddy suddenly 6 jumped / was jumping in through the window and sat on Mr. Marley. Seconds later, the car was in the lake. Fortunately, both Mr. Marley and Buddy are fine.

2 Complete. Then say what you were doing when something happened.

1 The sun shine ......was shining...... when they leave ......left...... the house.
2 We read .... when the train suddenly stop ....
3 I celebrate .... when my aunt call .... me.
4 The children sleep .... when the storm start ....
5 We swim .... when we see .... the shark.

3 Write a newspaper article about a storm. Include a title.

Wednesday, February 13

....

People were .... when the ....

A boy .... when ....

The lifeboat ....

The ....

Why do people enjoy newspaper articles?

Lesson 3
Telling Stories

1 Write another phrase for each part. Then choose, write, and act out.

miss dinner / fail the test / find the movie theater / ....

try again / ask someone / call my dad / ....

Are we going to .... ?

Don't worry. We can ....

2 **Read the story in your Student Book. Check (✓) *journal* or *dialogue*.**

Which text ...	journal	dialogue
1 ... is written in the past?	☐	☐
2 ... tells you what happens more clearly?	☐	☐
3 ... is more exciting?	☐	☐
4 ... tells you more about how people are feeling?	☐	☐

3 **Write *true* or *false*.**

1 The passengers on the deck know what to do. ....false........

2 Men have to get in the lifeboat last. ....

3 The lady in the green coat doesn't want to be saved. ....

4 The man who pushes in front of Amy is scared. ....

5 Amy is worried about her journal. ....

4 **What was Amy doing that evening before the *Titanic* hit the iceberg? Think and write her journal.**

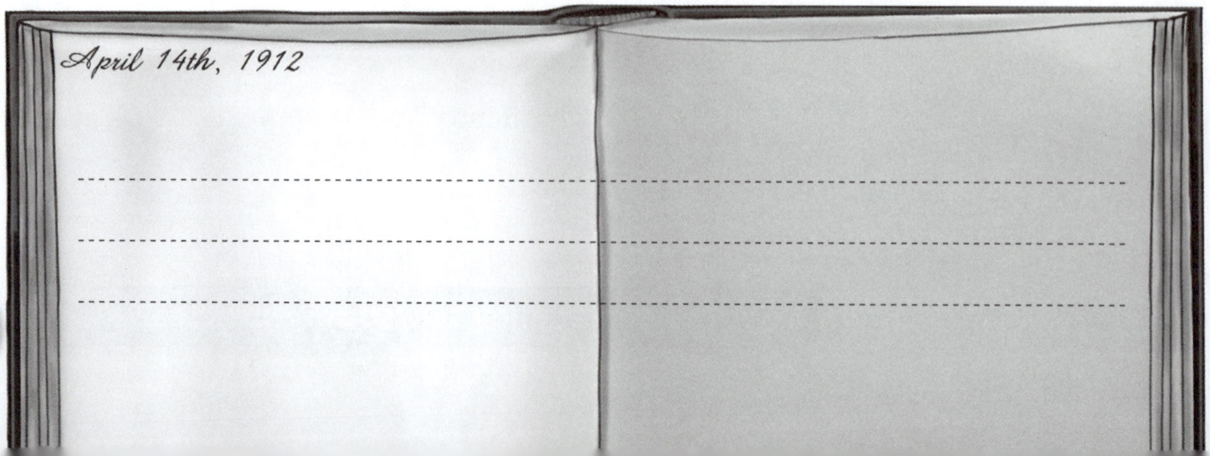

1 **What was Aunt Edith doing and how did she feel? Imagine and make notes.**

What happened?	What was Aunt Edith doing?	Feelings
Everyone was in the restaurant. A man knocked on the door. They saw the iceberg. A man pushed in front. The *Titanic* sank.	eating dinner	happy

2 **Write the sentences as a playscript.**

1 "Are we safe now?" asked Amy. Amy: Are we safe now?

2 "Where's my journal?" asked Amy. ....

3 "Look at that iceberg!" said the girl. ....

4 Aunt Edith said, "I'm cold so I'm going inside." ....

5 The officer shouted, "Come to the boat deck!" ....

3 **Imagine you're a TV reporter interviewing Aunt Edith. Write your questions and her answers in your notebook. Use the Story Creator.**

Story Creator

What happened when you were ...?
What did you hear/see ...?
How did you feel when you saw/heard ...?
Did you think ...?

I was ... when ...
I got up/shouted ...
I was very cold/scared ...
I thought we were going to ...

4 **Connect to Me**

Has anyone helped you when you were in trouble? How did you feel?

.... helped me when ....

I ....

Lesson 5

1 Circle.

I'm really interested in the *Titanic* story. No one knows how many passengers were traveling on the ship **1 when / while** it sank. Why? Because some people didn't buy tickets. They were called "stowaways" and they got onto the ship **2 while / when** it was preparing to leave. **3 While / When** the crew on the ship weren't looking, they found places to hide. Some of the stowaways were probably hiding **4 when / while** the ship hit the iceberg. It was scary for them. **5 While / When** the accident happened, they were thinking about their new life.

2 **Complete with *when* or *while*.**

1 The teacher was talking ....while.......... you were looking out of the window.

2 What were they doing .... the door opened?

3 .... you were playing the piano, I left the room.

4 .... the bell rang, you were eating your lunch.

5 What were you doing .... I was looking for my bag?

3 **Write about what happened at home last night. Then tell a friend.**

Last night, I was watching TV when ....

While my mom/dad/brother .... , I was ....

I was ....

When I ....

Last night, I was watching TV when the dog broke a vase.

1 Complete.

captain flag float pirates destroy mast holes ~~waves~~

It was stormy and the 1 waves *were high when we saw the big ship. A Japanese* 2 .... *was flying from the ship's* 3 .... *The* 4 .... *was on the ship with his men. They didn't know it, but their lives were in danger. We were* 5 .... *and we were planning to* 6 .... *their ship. Then we saw a boy who was swimming near us. While our ship was getting closer, he was making* 7 .... *in it. Water started to come in! I took a big piece of wood and jumped into the ocean. At least I could* 8 .... *with the wood ...*

2 Write the answers to the quiz. Then ask and answer.

1 The opposite of *sink*. float

2 The most important person on the ship. ....

3 The opposite of *make*. ....

4 A person who steals things from ships. ....

5 It's made of cotton or silk and is different for every country. ....

The opposite of *sink*.

Float.

Spelling Central

Irregular plurals

3 Complete the puzzle with the plural forms. What's the hidden word?

1 mouse	5 scarf
2 tooth	6 life
3 wife	7 man
4 person	

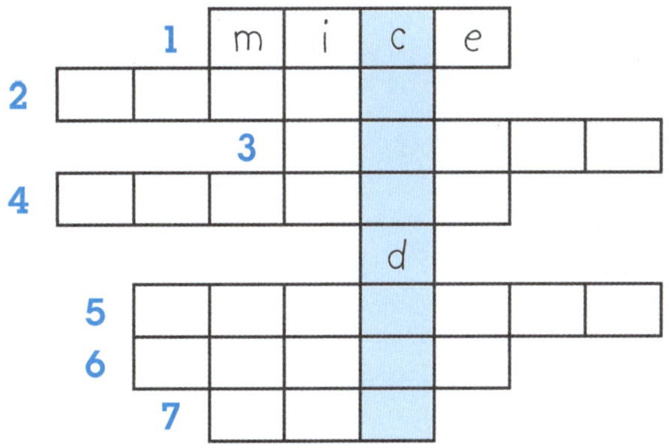

Hidden word: ....

Lesson 7
CLIL

1 **Read and write *true* or *false*.**

Would You Like to Live in an Iceberg?

Antarctica is beautiful, and more people visit it every year. A big new building is being designed there, inside an enormous iceberg! Trucks that are used for moving snow cut big holes in the floating ice to make rooms. There are going to be bedrooms for a hundred people, bathrooms, a kitchen, and a big hall.

After about ten years, everyone is going to have to leave. When the iceberg melts, the building is destroyed. But anything left when the ice melts can be used for a new iceberg home.

1 Fewer people go to Antarctica now than in the past. ___false___
2 There's a new building on top of an iceberg. ________
3 To create rooms, big holes are made in the ice by trucks. ________
4 There's going to be somewhere to eat in the iceberg building. ________
5 Everything is destroyed when the ice melts. ________

2 **Use your Student Book research to make an Info Card. Write about global warming and sea levels.**

Find Out More!

What is it? What happens? Why?
sea levels polar ice caps icebergs animals

3 **Do an experiment to find out what happens when ice melts.**

Try it Out

- Pour some water into a glass. What will happen when you add ice cubes?
- Put ice cubes in the glass. Mark the water level with a pen. Take a picture. What will happen when the ice melts?
- Wait for the ice cubes to melt. Is the water level higher, lower, or the same as before? Take a picture.

4 **Select and store information on this topic in the Class Info Hub.**

GRAND QUIZ CENTRAL

1 Play with a friend. Choose a character.
2 Write a new question to ask your friend.
3 Take turns asking. Say the answer, then write it in your notebook.
4 If a question is too hard, you can swap! Choose and check (✔) up to three questions. Remember: each swap loses a bonus point!

	Questions to ask Pirate Captain	Questions to ask Rescue Hero
1	How much of an iceberg is above the water?	What happens to the water level when an ice cube melts?
2	What were you doing when the teacher walked into the room?	What were you doing when your class ended for lunch?
3	What's another word for *rescue*?	What's the opposite of *float*?
4	In the story, what was Amy doing when she heard the loud noise?	In the story, what was Amy doing when the iceberg passed the *Titanic*?
5	*When* or *while*? *He was doing his homework … his cell phone rang.*	*When* or *while*? *… she was baking a cake, she dropped the eggs.*
6	What's the plural of *man*?	What's the singular of *lives*?
7	Complete: *When the Titanic was sailing to America, it …*	Complete: *While Amy was waiting in line, a man …*
8	What was Angelo doing while the others were reading the story?	What was Rufus doing while he was looking up the *Titanic* on the internet?
9	Unscramble this word: *voriuvsr*	Unscramble this word: *fbtoalie*
10	....?	....?

Check your friend's answers. Then color your life jackets and write your score.

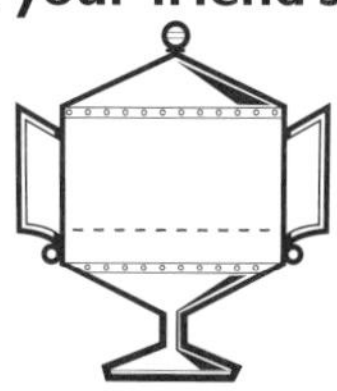

Now choose your title:

- ☐ **Quiz Master!** I understand this topic well.
- ☐ **Quiz Improver!** I don't understand everything.
- ☐ **Quiz Beginner!** I need some help.

Chapter 7 Let's Cook!

Lesson 1

1 Look and complete.

slice fry oil pan pour chop pepper ~~boil~~

1 ___Boil___ the water!

2 ________ the lemon!

3 ________ the milk!

4 ________ the onions in the 5 ________!

6 ________ the potatoes!

7 Wash the ________!

8 Grind the ________!

2 Write *true* or *false*.

1 You slice onions with a spoon. ___false___

2 You boil water and then you cook the pasta. ________

3 A pan is usually made of metal. ________

4 You can't chop peppers into small pieces. ________

5 You usually fry food in oil. ________

3 Tell a friend what you do in the kitchen.

I wash the pans, but I don't like it!

I slice the tomatoes for a salad.

4 Choose a way to categorize the new words in your notebook.

1 Complete with the correct adverbs.

careful ~~quick~~ slow loud good easy

Charlie: We have to make dinner **1** ....quickly.... because I have a lot of homework.

Olivia: What about a rice salad? We can do it **2** .... – it's simple.

Charlie: Great. Why don't you boil the water? Then add the rice. It has to cook **3** .... but we have time. I'm going to chop the peppers.

Olivia: But it's boring cooking the rice. I want to chop the peppers!

Charlie: Stop talking so **4** .... I'm standing next to you.

Olivia: But you always tell me what to do. I'm shouting because I'm angry and I don't cook **5** .... when I'm angry.

Charlie: Calm down and chop the peppers. Do it **6** .... , please!

2 Complete with an appropriate adverb. Then ask and answer.

1 Do you cook .... ?

2 Do you play music .... ?

3 Do you ride your bike .... ?

4 Do you talk .... ?

5 Do you eat your food .... ?

3 Complete the instructions for a recipe. Include adverbs.

Vegetable Soup

1 First, ... the onions and carrots .... the tomatoes into small pieces.

2 .... the vegetables in the oil ....

3 Then, ... the water. Add the hot water .... !

4 Cook the soup .... for two hours.

5 Add salt and pepper and serve the soup ....

What is important to remember when you write instructions?

Lesson 3
Telling Stories

1 **Check (✓) a sentence that's true for you. Then complete and act out.**

I can't play basketball. ☐ I can't write a poem. ☐ I can't take pictures. ☐

I can't ....

Anyone can .... Let me help you.

2 **Read the story in your Student Book. Check (✓) the most important thing Picture 2 tells us about Mrs. Kapoor.**

1 She really loves food. ☐
2 She really likes her neighbor. ☐
3 She's very proud of her sons. ☐

3 **Write: Mrs. Kapoor, Kuntal, Shabar, or Rashmi.**

1 Who wants the house to look nice? ......Mrs. Kapoor....
2 Who's the youngest of Mrs. Kapoor's children? ....
3 Who's Kuntal's younger brother? ....
4 Who's cooking for the family that night? ....
5 Who's Maa? ....
6 Who is taller than she used to be? ....

4 **What's Rashmi doing in the kitchen? Think and write.**

1 What are good things about the brothers' cooking? Make notes.

Shabar

works for best bakery in Paris

Kuntal

2 Find the opposite and write the letter. Then complete the sentences with an appropriate adverb in the correct place.

quickly [c] smartly [ ] well [ ] loudly [ ] happily [ ]

a badly **b** sadly **c** slowly **d** stupidly **e** quietly

1 He (slowly) stirred the curry.

2 She shouted when she saw her sons.

3 Cook it so that it's delicious.

4 They ate because they were hungry.

3 Write a speech in your notebook persuading Shabar and Kuntal to eat something you've made. Use the Story Creator.

Story Creator

The recipe is ...

I use the best/most expensive ...

I carefully/quickly ...

Then I pour/bake ...

You haven't seen/eaten ...

In my opinion, it's the most delicious/ amazing ...

You're going to ...

I'm the best ...

4 Connect to Me

Have you eaten food from other countries? Which was your favorite?

Lesson 5

1 **Complete Yasmin's food diary. Use *too much, too many,* or *enough*.**

Week 1

I've decided to keep a food diary so that I know when I'm eating the wrong things and not drinking **1** ....enough.... water. Monday was awful because I ate **2** .... bread. On Tuesday, I drank a lot of water but I didn't eat **3** .... vegetables. On Wednesday, I ate **4** .... strawberries and had a stomach ache! I ate a lot of fruit and vegetables on Thursday. Today it's Friday, and it's Angelo's party. I'm going to eat **5** .... chips and drink **6** .... cola, but it is the weekend!

2 **Unscramble and write. True or false for you? Tell a friend.**

1 eat / . / much / chocolate / too / I ....

2 I / enough / . / fruit / always / eat ....

3 doesn't / water / drink / She / . / enough ....

4 too / eat / cookies / many / I / . ...

I eat too much chocolate. That's true but I also eat a lot of fruit and vegetables.

I don't eat much chocolate but I eat too much ice cream.

3 **Write your own food diary for the past three days. Use *too much, too many, enough,* or *not enough*.**

On .... , I ate ....

On .... , I ate ....

but I didn't drink ....

Last night, I ....

I ....

1 **Unscramble and write.**

★ What's your favorite sandwich? Our winning recipe this week. ★

My favorite sandwich is a peanut butter and jelly banana dog. You need good, **1** ftos ____soft____ bread – don't use old, hard bread. Add your favorite jelly and some **2** unycrch ____________ peanut butter. The sandwich **3** ssllme ____________ great because of the banana and the fruity jelly. When you **4** tseat ____________ it, you get a mix of flavors. First, there's the **5** twese ____________ jelly and banana and then the peanut butter which is **6** tylsa ____________ . Sometimes I have mine with some **7** iuycj ____________ strawberries. Try it! It's a **8** ttyas ____________ and healthy sandwich!

2 **Write the name of a food or drink for each group. Then compare ideas with a friend.**

1 smelly ____blue cheese____ **4** not very tasty ____________

2 juicy ____________ **5** sour ____________

3 soft ____________ **6** bitter ____________

I think that blue cheese is very smelly.

Spelling Central

Adjectives ending in -y

3 **Find and circle nouns with adjectives that end in *y*. Then write.**

s	n	o	w	t	f
m	o	c	l	a	r
e	i	y		s	u
l	s			t	i
l	e	i	c	e	t
h	e	a	l	t	h

noun	adjective
ice	icy

Lesson 7

CLIL

taste Japanese delicious chefs ~~bitter~~ salty

1 Read and complete.

We know that food can be sweet, salty, **1** ......bitter...... , or sour. But do you know what umami is? Umami means "tasty/ yummy" in **2** .... It's a flavor that's found in meat, mushrooms, seaweed, and "smelly" foods like cheese. It makes everything taste better and everyone likes it, even babies! A lot of Asian food tastes of umami and that is why it's so **3** ....
Food is often tastier when you add salt. But it isn't good to eat too much **4** .... food so **5** .... are now using umami. It can make food **6** .... really good.

2 Use your Student Book research to make an Info Card. Write about how your other senses affect how you taste food.

Find Out More!

seeing smelling feeling hearing touching

3 Do a group experiment to find out the effect of your other senses on taste.

Try it Out

- Tie a scarf around your eyes. Taste mayonnaise, yogurt, and apple sauce. Can you tell the difference?
- Eat a potato chip. Now cover your ears and eat another chip. Is it more or less crunchy?
- Pinch your nose. Eat small pieces of apple, carrot, and pear. Do they taste different?
- Hold a slice of lemon under your nose. Eat small pieces of apple, carrot, and pear. Can you tell what they are?

4 Select and store information on this topic in the Class Info Hub.

GRAND QUIZ CENTRAL

1 Play with a friend. Choose a character.
2 Write a new question to ask your friend.
3 Take turns asking. Say the answer, then write it in your notebook.
4 If a question is too hard, you can swap! Choose and check (✔) up to three questions. Remember: each swap loses a bonus point!

	Questions to ask Crunchmaster	Questions to ask Supertaster

1	Which foods are smelly: *cheese, fish, carrots?*	Which foods are soft: *bananas, apples, yogurt?*
2	Turn this word into an adverb: *hungry*	Turn this word into an adverb: *happy*
3	How should you use a knife so you don't cut your finger?	How should you slice vegetables so they cook quickly?
4	In the story, what was Shabar's cookie bird holding in its beak?	In the story, what did Kuntal put on top of his curry?
5	Complete: *Yasmin thinks potato chips have … salt on them.*	Complete: *Yasmin thinks Angelo doesn't eat … fruit and vegetables.*
6	Turn this word into an adjective: *sport*	Turn this word into an adjective: *rain*
7	What do you add with salt to make food tasty?	How does food taste when you add sugar to it?
8	What do you eat too much of?	What don't you eat enough of?
9	Unscramble this word: *rcuynch*	Unscramble this word: *uyjic*
10	______________________?	______________________?

Check your friend's answers. Then color your chef's hats and write your score.

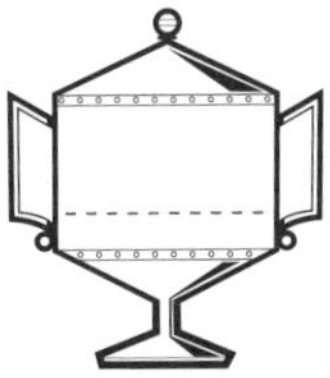

Now choose your title:

- ☐ **Quiz Master!** I understand this topic well.
- ☐ **Quiz Improver!** I don't understand everything.
- ☐ **Quiz Beginner!** I need some help.

Chapter 8

Speak Out!

Lesson 1

1 Solve the clues and complete the words.

1 say something to someone: tell

2 say that another person is wrong: d..................

3 speak to someone angrily: a..................

4 say something that isn't true: l..................

5 say that another person is right: a..................

6 something funny you say or do: j..................

7 choose what you're going to do: d..................

8 do this when something is funny: l..................

9 give some of what you have to someone:
s..................

10 treat someone well, like a parent or teacher: r..................

11 let a person know you can give them something: o..................

2 Write answers for you. Then ask and answer the questions.

1 When did you last argue? ....

2 Do you sometimes lie? Why? ....

3 Would you share your last piece of chocolate? ....

4 Who do you respect? Why? ....

5 Do you know a good joke? ....

When did you last argue?

I argued with my brother last night.

3 Choose a way to categorize the new words in your notebook.

Lesson 2

1 Write.

1 "I have a dog named Muffin."

She told us she had a dog named Muffin.

2 "I hate broccoli."

She joked ....

3 "Schools need more computers."

She explained ....

4 "I can't dance very well."

She said ....

5 "Free time is important for students."

She agreed ....

2 Write. Ask and answer with a friend. Then tell the class.

	favorite hobby and why	favorite food and why	favorite song and why
Me			
My friend			

3 Your favorite actor was on TV last night. Write an email telling a friend about it.

TO: Jake

Hi, ...

I saw .... on TV last night. It was really interesting.

He/She said that ....

He/She joked that ....

He/She explained that ....

He/She ....

Bye for now.

....

What kind of information makes an email interesting?

Lesson 3
Telling Stories

1 Write another correct word. Then choose, complete, and act out.

disagree / respect / argue / ....

How / you / say "..................." in .... ?

It's ....

Sorry! What / you / say?

I said it was " ...."

2 Read the story in your Student Book. Circle the words that describe the story. Then check (✓) the story type.

travel funny strange creatures historical imaginary horror unusual place true

fantasy adventure ☐ factual biography ☐ **comedy** ☐

3 **Write answers.**

1 Why can't Gulliver move when he wakes up? He's tied with rope.

2 How does he feel? ....

3 What's Gulliver doing when they take him to the temple?

....

4 Where do the little people say Gulliver is from?

....

4 How did Gulliver travel to Lilliput? Check (✓) the correct options.

I, Lemuel Gulliver, ...

☐ *walked.*

☐ *sailed in a ship.*

☐ *flew by helicopter.*

☐ *fell from the stars.*

☐ *swam in the ocean.*

☐ *arrived by taxi.*

1 **Compare Gulliver and the Emperor of Lilliput. Make notes.**

Gulliver

is very ......tall...... .

speaks ....

eats ....

doesn't want ....

thinks the emperor ....

....

The Emperor of Lilliput

is very ....

speaks ......Lillputian...... .

eats ....

doesn't want ....

thinks Gulliver ....

....

2 **Complete the sentences with *joke*, *argue*, *tell*, or *say*. Then write what each person actually said.**

Writing Tools

1 I .... I was hungry. ......"I'm hungry."......

2 He .... me he couldn't help. ....

3 He .... that I wore funny clothes. ....

4 I .... it was a bad idea. ....

3 **Write a dialogue between Gulliver and the Emperor in your notebook. Use the Story Creator.**

Story Creator

"Why do you think/argue ...?"

"We believe that everyone should ..."

"We don't want to speak/fight ..."

"I think it's important/silly ..."

"Why don't you try/eat ...?"

"We/You all like ..."

"But we can't agree/explain ..."

"Can I suggest/ask ...?"

"So can we/you agree/offer to ...?"

4 **Connect to Me**

Have you ever argued about something that wasn't important?

I argued with .... about ....

Later, I thought ....

Lesson 5

1 Underline the reported questions. Then complete the direct speech.

I asked Rufus if he knew another good story about Gulliver and he told me to read one about Laputa. I asked why Laputa was a good story. He explained it was about a flying island. I asked what happened in the story. He said the Laputans knew many facts, but weren't clever. They loved to study math, but they weren't good at building houses. Then he asked me why I didn't just read the book. So I asked him why I should read it. I said that I knew the story already!

1 Do you know .... another good story about Gulliver?

2 .... Laputa a good story?

3 .... in the story?

4 .... you just read the book?

5 .... I read it?

2 Write the reported questions. Then tell a friend how the people responded.

1 I / my dad / if / likes cooking I asked my dad if he liked cooking.

2 I / my mom / who / her favorite actor ....

3 She / me / where / I want to go ....

4 My friend / me / what happens ....

5 He / me / which / soccer team / like ....

I asked my dad if he liked cooking. He explained that he didn't because he always burned the food!

3 Write about a conversation with a friend.

A: Are you going to .... ?

B: ....

A: Can I .... ?

B: ....

My friend asked me ....

He/She asked if ....

I told him/her that ....

I said that ....

1 Complete.

accent understand ~~repeat~~ mean signs pronounce

Harry: Hi, Francesca. It's Harry.

Francesca: Sorry, can you **1** ......repeat...... your name? I can't hear you.

Harry: It's Harry ... I'm at home ... in New York.

Francesca: Oh, Harry, hi. It's your American **2** .... It's difficult to **3** ....

Harry: I'll speak slowly. Hey, I'm coming to see you on Thursday.

Francesca: That's nice. Do you **4** .... Tuesday or Thursday?

Harry: Thursday. You **5** .... it "Thursday". Don't worry. We can use **6** .... to talk when I get there!

2 Write answers. Then ask and answer.

1 What words do you find difficult to pronounce in English?

....

2 What's your favorite accent? ....

3 What body language can you see in the class right now?

....

4 What makes you smile? ....

What words do you find difficult to pronounce in English?

Encyclopedia and Wednesday!

Spelling Central

Words ending in silent –e

3 Unscramble the words. Use the colored squares to write the hidden message.

~~heme~~	nein	feiv
verrai	crei	semuo
seu	leta	

Hidden message:

H.............. **a** .... **!**

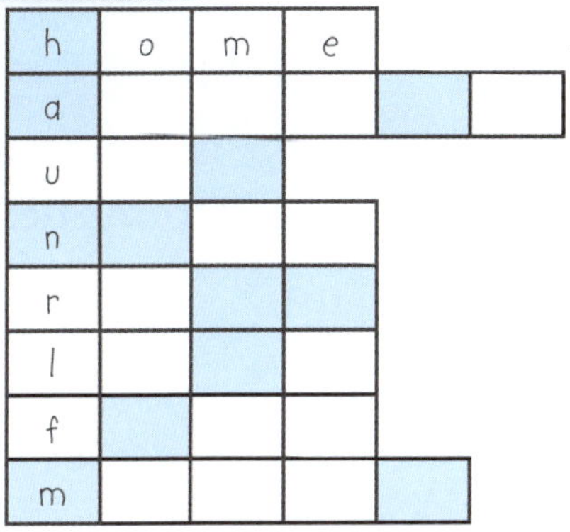

Lesson 7 CLIL

translate speak pronounce story ~~languages~~ understand

1 Read and complete.

The author J. R. R. Tolkien wrote fantasy books full of strange creatures. He invented a group of **1** languages called "Elvish." They were spoken by characters called elves and created just for his books. Tolkien said that the language was the first thing he imagined for a book. He created the world and the **2** ____________ after that.

Some people have studied Elvish so that they can **3** ____________ to each other. They use websites that explain how to **4** ____________ Elvish sounds. There are also online dictionaries that **5** ____________ Elvish into your own language. Elvish is not easy to **6** ____________ but it's a very cool language!

2 Use your Student Book research to make an Info Card. Write about your language and where it's spoken in the world.

where how many people other languages second language

Find Out More!

3 Make a language map.

Try it Out

- Trace or photocopy a world map.
- Color the places where your language is spoken.
- Think of other languages. Use a different color for the place each language is spoken.
- Make a key on the map to show what the colors mean.
- Do you know "hello" in other languages? Write each word in the correct country.

4 Select and store information on this topic in the Class Info Hub.

GRAND QUIZ CENTRAL

1 Play with a friend. Choose a character.
2 Write a new question to ask your friend.
3 Take turns asking. Say the answer, then write it in your notebook.
4 If a question is too hard, you can swap! Choose and check (✔) up to three questions. Remember: each swap loses a bonus point!

	Questions to ask Chatterbox	Questions to ask Big Mouth
1	Say in your language *I don't understand.*	Say in your language *Please speak more slowly.*
2	What did the author ask Rufus about reading?	What did Rufus ask the author about ideas?
3	What's the opposite of *tell the truth*?	What's the opposite of *agree*?
4	Change to reported speech: *"What's your name?" she asked.*	Change to reported speech: *"Do you like adventure stories?" he asked.*
5	Which word has a silent -e? *pronounce, accent, speak*	Which word has a silent -e? *mean, understand, translate*
6	Change to direct speech: *He explained that he didn't want it.*	Change to direct speech: *She agreed that it was a beautiful dress.*
7	In the story, what did Lilliputians and Blefuscudians argue about?	In the story, what did Gulliver and the Emperor disagree about?
8	What's the most spoken language in the world?	What's the third most spoken language in the world?
9	Unscramble this word: *trsecep*	Unscramble this word: *apetre*
10	....?	....?

Check your friend's answers. Then color your speech bubbles and write your score.

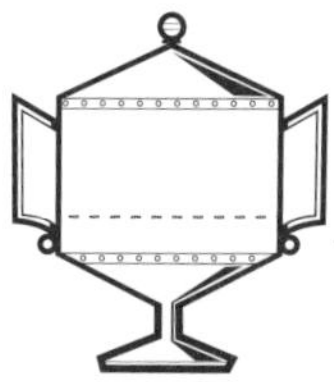

Now choose your title:

- ☐ **Quiz Master!** I understand this topic well.
- ☐ **Quiz Improver!** I don't understand everything.
- ☐ **Quiz Beginner!** I need some help.

Chapter 9 Into the Future

Lesson 1

1 **Unscramble and write the words.**

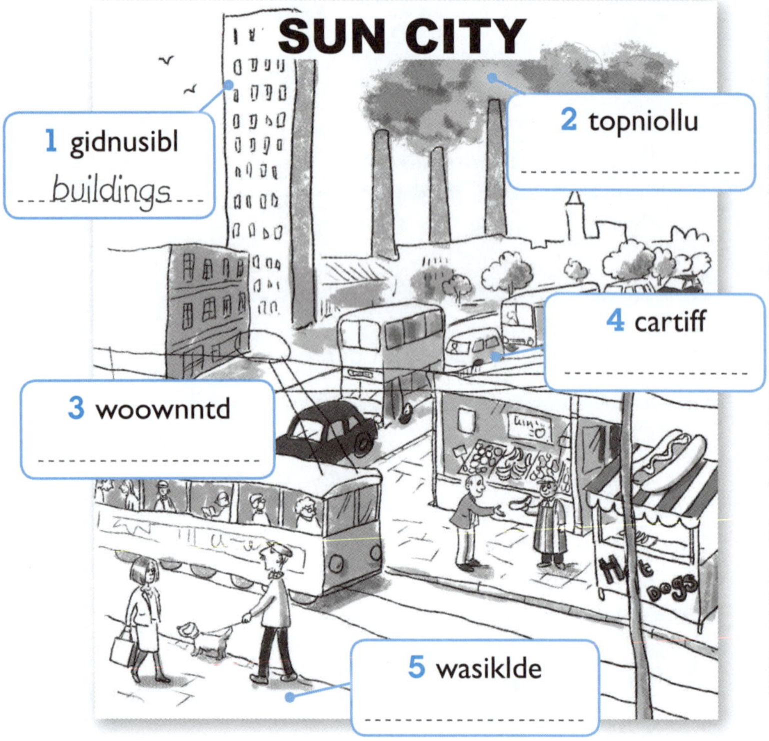

2 **Write *true* or *false*.**

1 A tram uses electricity to move. true

2 A town isn't as big as a village. ______

3 Pollution makes the air very clean. ______

4 There's more traffic in a city than in a village. ______

5 There's usually more wildlife in natural areas. ______

3 **Circle the words in Activity 1 that describe where you live. Tell a friend.**

There's too much traffic.

It's a very pretty village.

4 **Choose a way to categorize the new words in your notebook.**

1 **What will life be like in Skytopia? Complete with *will* or *won't* and the correct verb.**

have
walk
~~live~~
be
fly
grow
be

1 People ......will live...... in very tall buildings.

2 Children .... to school – they .... to school!

3 Flowers .... in the sky.

4 The air .... cleaner. There .... any pollution.

5 People .... more free time in Skytopia!

2 **Choose six verbs and write sentences about you. Talk to a friend.**

live buy have go drive travel meet be wear

....

....

....

3 **Check (✓) the features that would be in your perfect town. Then write your competition entry.**

nice buildings	☐	good houses	☐	not too much traffic	☐
no pollution	☐	bike paths	☐	....	☐
swimming pools	☐	parks	☐	....	☐

In my perfect town, there will ....

....

There won't ....

People will ....

It ....

How can you make your competition entry the best?

Lesson 3
Telling Stories

1 Cross out the incorrect word. Then choose, complete, and act out.

tired / scared / amazing / bored

What's the matter?

I'm ....

Why don't you .... ? ...

2 **Read the story in your Student Book. Check (✓) the sentences that describe the story. Then circle the story type.**

1 It's about science and technology in the future. ☐

2 What happens to Dax couldn't really happen now. ☐

3 The story is about a boy at school in real life. ☐

science fiction   *fairy tale*   factual / non-fiction

3 **Circle.**

1 Dax visits the doctor because he needs **more** / **less** memory space.

2 Dax needs to learn **facts about brains** / **information about planets**.

3 At the Memory Bank, his old memories are **stored on a chip** / **lost in space**.

4 When Dax can't remember his address, he feels **confused** / **angry**.

5 Dax will go back to the Memory Bank **before** / **after** his exam.

4 **What memories are stored on Dax's chip? Think and write.**

Lesson 4
Time to Think

1 **Compare Dax's memories and yours. Make notes.**

Dax's Memories

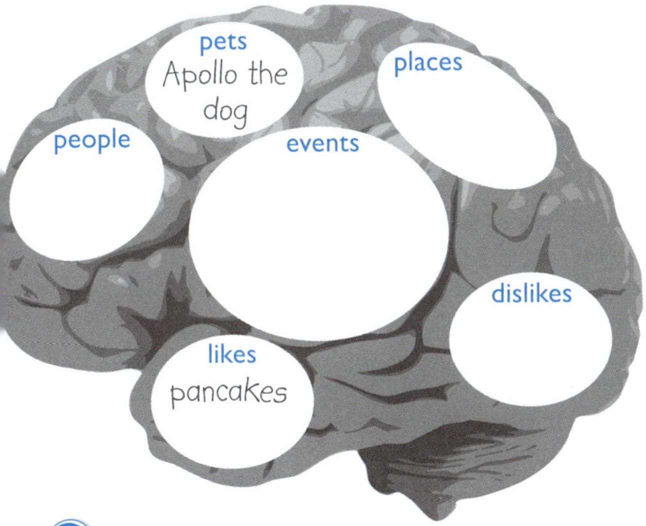

My Memories

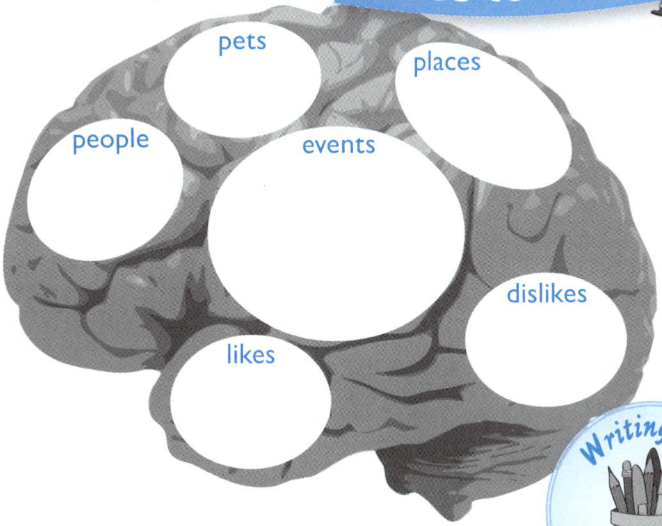

2 **Draw lines to make sentences.**

1 A space academy is a school		a the K2 sky tram goes.
2 A doctor is a person	who	b is part of our solar system.
3 A computer is a machine		c you can send email from.
4 Mars is a planet	where	d you can learn about planets.
5 Mia is a student		e takes care of people.
6 Kepler is the village	that	f goes to the academy.

3 **Write about your memories in your notebook. Use the Story Creator.**

Story Creator

When I was young …

I remember when I was …

My best/earliest memory is …

I remember eating/going to …

I will never forget …

… is the place where … lived/was.

I used to like to play/eat …

… because it was fun/important …

It was amazing/sad …

4 **Connect to Me**

Have things ever gone wrong when you've tried to help someone?

I tried to .... but ....

I felt ....

Lesson 5

1 Complete what Hamish is thinking. You can use the phrases more than once.

~~what will~~	who will	will	won't	will
how will	where will	what will		

1 ....What will.... life be like for dogs in the future? I think a robot will take care of me. Will it remember to feed me? Hmm. 2 .... they ever stop talking about computers? 3 .... take me for a walk this afternoon? 4 .... we go? To the village? To see wildlife in the park? Hmm. Where will I find something to eat in this place? WHAT'S THAT? 5 .... it taste like? Will it still be there when we come back? 6 .... they see that it's missing? No, they 7 .... ! I'll just eat it while no one is looking! 8 .... anyone know?

2 Unscramble and write. Then ask and answer.

1 buildings / future / What / like / in / will / the / look / ?

....

2 be / ? / What / on / will / TV

....

3 will / eat / What / ? / you

....

4 will / Where / on / ? / go / you / vacation

....

What will buildings look like in the future?

Buildings will be big and silver with unusual shapes.

3 Write questions and predictions about next year.

travel	friends	school	family	hobbies

Will I .... ? ....

How .... ? ....

Who .... ? ....

Where .... ? ....

1 Complete.

touch screen controls
~~solar panels~~
wireless
driverless
recyclable

How Cool Will Your sChOOL Be?

I think my school will be better in the future. It'll have 1 solar panels on the roof to save money. We'll have 2 ________ in the classrooms that are fun to use but won't break! The school will also give us 3 ________ pens and paper because they're better for the planet. Our computers will be 4 ________ so that we can use them anywhere in the school. I hope the uniform will be more fashionable, too. Finally, I think my school will use electric buses but they won't be 5 ________ .

2 Check (✓) if you agree or cross (✗) if you disagree. Then talk to a friend.

1 My town will have wind turbines. ☐
2 We will only use rechargeable batteries. ☐
3 Trains and trams will be driverless. ☐
4 All clothes will be recyclable. ☐
5 We'll have more gadgets in the future. ☐

I think my town will have wind turbines.

I don't think it will. Wind turbines are very expensive.

Spelling Central

Suffixes *–able* and *–less*

3 Use the code to find the first part of the word. Then complete the word with the correct suffix: *–able* or *–less*.

	1	2	3	4	5	6	7
A	s	f	w	k	y	e	t
B	o	r	l	b	g	j	n
C	i	a	v	h	c	d	m

a 3A, 1C, 2B, 6A … wireless
b 2B, 6A, 5C, 5A, 5C, 3B … ________
c 5C, 1B, 7C, 2A, 1B, 2B, 7A … ________
d 6C, 2B, 1C, 3C, 6A, 2B … ________

Lesson 7
CLIL

1 **Read and circle.**

Everyone has **1 the same** / **a different** face, fingerprints, eyes, and voice. Biometric systems use this information to recognize who **2 something** / **someone** is. "Face recognition" is already used for **3 passports** / **library books**. A picture is taken of your face and a computer looks at its shape and size, the color of your eyes, how long your nose is, and how big your mouth is. Then the information is stored on a big computer. It's also stored on a **4 chip** / **computer** inside the passport so that no one else can **5 steal** / **use** it.

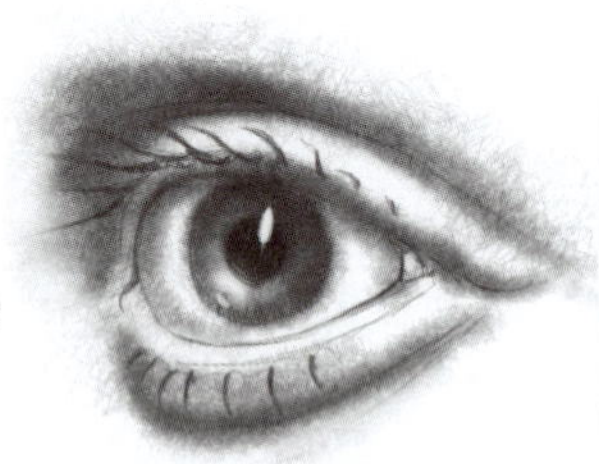

In the **6 future** / **past** , more biometric gadgets will be used in houses. Touch screen controls will be used more for reading fingerprints. And you might be able to open the door and turn on the TV just with your face!

2 **Use your Student Book research to make an Info Card. Write about what people want in their homes in the future.**

Find Out More!

bathroom kitchen bedroom garden
useful entertaining energy saving

3 **Design a house for the future.**

Try it Out

- In groups, choose a person or people to design your home for.
- Plan your home. How will people use each room? What will they need? What will be in your house for the future?
- Draw your home.

4 **Select and store information on this topic in the Class Info Hub.**

GRAND QUIZ CENTRAL

1 Play with a friend. Choose a character.
2 Write a new question to ask your friend.
3 Take turns asking. Say the answer, then write it in your notebook.
4 If a question is too hard, you can swap! Choose and check (✔) up to three questions. Remember: each swap loses a bonus point!

	Questions to ask Wireless Warrior	Questions to ask Recharger
1	What does traffic create?	What's a word for plants, birds, and animals?
2	What kind of biometric system does Living Tomorrow use to open doors?	What kind of biometric system is used in passports?
3	Name one thing you'll have in your home in the future.	Name one thing you'll do after you leave school.
4	Complete: *What … schools be like in the future?*	Complete: *Will we … cars in the future?*
5	In Rufus's opinion, why won't we need paper in the future?	In Rufus's opinion, where will we live in the future?
6	Give the opposite: *People will live on the moon.*	Give the opposite: *We won't be able to store our memories.*
7	Give an example of a word that ends with *–able*.	Give an example of a word that ends with *–less*.
8	In the story, where do Dax and Mia study?	In the story, where does Dr. Munro work?
9	Unscramble this word: *dawksile*	Unscramble this word: *wnodontw*
10	------------------------------------ ?	------------------------------------ ?

Check your friend's answers. Then color your batteries and write your score.

Now choose your title:

- ☐ **Quiz Master!** I understand this topic well.
- ☐ **Quiz Improver!** I don't understand everything.
- ☐ **Quiz Beginner!** I need some help.

Chapter 1 Review

1 Reading and Writing.

Look and read. Write *yes* or *no*.

Examples.

The girls near the tree are playing with hula hoops. ......yes......

It's five to eleven. ......no......

1 The boy sitting under the tree is reading an encyclopedia. ....

2 The teacher in the skirt is ringing the school bell. ....

3 The boys in shorts are playing soccer. ....

4 The man in glasses is writing on the chalkboard. ....

5 The girl with long hair is eating an apple. ....

2 Listening.

Listen and check ✓ the correct picture.

Example. What time did Jake arrive at school?

a  ✓

b 

c 

1 What does Jake have in his bag?

a 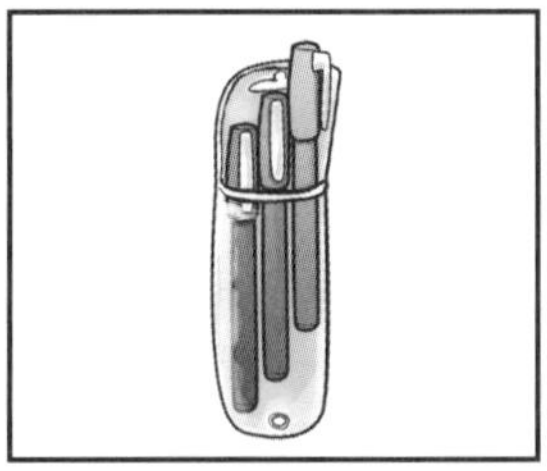

b 

c 

2 What's Kate doing after school today?

a 

b 

c 

3 What does Jake want to buy?

a 

b 

c 

Chapter 2 Review

1 Reading and Writing.

Ben and Emily are talking at a chess club after school.
What does Emily say? Write the letters.

> Example.
>
> **Ben:** Hi, Emily. I haven't seen you here before. How long have you played chess?
> **Emily:** ......c.......

1 **Ben:** How often do you play?
Emily: ....

2 **Ben:** What other hobbies do you have?
Emily: ....

3 **Ben:** Are you going to be in the chess competition?
Emily: ....

a	No, I don't think I have time.
b	I want to, but it's at the same time as my karate class.
c	My dad taught me last summer. **(Example)**
d	Only on weekends because I don't have much time.
e	Yes, there are ten people here today.
f	I enjoy playing tennis and baking.

2 Listening.

Listen and write.

It's the cooking competition of the year!

Who can do it? school children in this town

1 When? from Sunday to ....

2 Where is it? .... Hotel

3 Competition starts: .... a.m.

4 Please cook something with: a red pepper, ... , and tomatoes

5 Cost (before Friday): ....

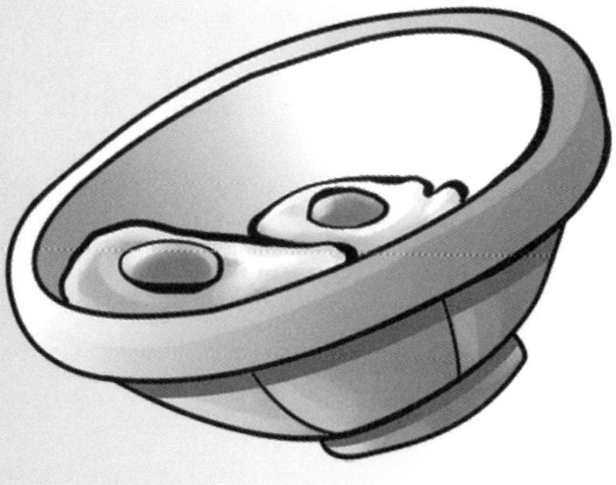

Chapter 3 Review

1 Reading and Writing.

Complete the story.

Example.

~~early~~ amazing well frightened was fell walking confusing

Last night, I went to bed ....early.... because I was very tired. I (1) .... asleep quickly and soon started dreaming. I was (2) .... around a big castle on the top of a mountain. It was snowing and it was just as cold inside the castle as it was outside. I was freezing. There were lots of different rooms with old chairs and tables. There weren't any other people, but I wasn't (3) .... .Then I saw something. There was a monkey in front of me. It was bigger than the monkeys at the zoo and it was carrying an (4) .... chocolate cake. "Happy Birthday! Would you like some cake?" it asked. I took some cake and the monkey disappeared. When I woke up, I was very confused!

5 Now check ☑ the best title for the story.

a A Cold Night ☐

b Oliver's Weird Dream ☐

c Oliver's Surprise Birthday ☐

2 Listening.

Listen and color, write, or draw.

Chapter 4 Review

1 Reading and Writing

Read and write the words.

Example.

~~a dictionary~~	spring	passenger	pilots	a picnic
a compass	February	a bridge	nurses	scarves

Example.

You use this when you want to find out what a word means. ......a dictionary......

1 Someone who travels from one place to another. ....

2 This is the second month of the year. ....

3 This is a place where you can cross a road or a river. ....

4 These are often worn around your neck when it's cold. ....

5 This is a type of meal that you can enjoy outdoors. ....

2 Listening.

What did each person give Jack for his skiing vacation?
Listen and write the letters.

cousin	d
brother	
best friend	
aunt	
dad	
James	

a

b

c

d
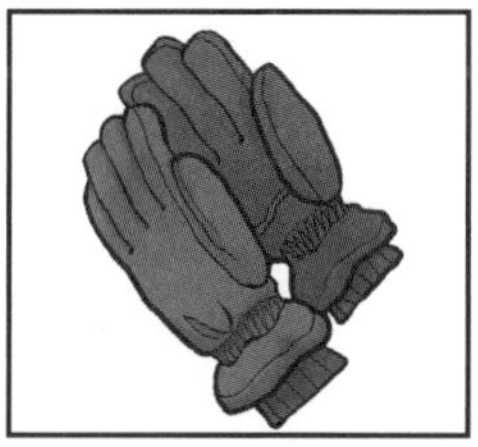

e

f

g

h

Chapter 5 Review

1 Reading and Writing.

Read and complete, with 1, 2, 3, or 4 words.

Alex Helps His Dad

It was winter and Alex's dad was working in the yard. "Alex, can you help me, please?" his dad asked. "There was a bad storm last night and I want to remove some of the old trees and plants from the yard." Alex wanted to stay inside and play a computer game with his friends. But he knew his dad needed him so he put on his warm coat and went outside. It was cold and windy. First, Alex and his dad collected the old trees, then they cut them up to have wood for their fire. Alex soon felt warmer. He found some old flowers and started to pull them out of the ground. Suddenly he saw something under the flowers. It was shining. At first he thought it was some glass or plastic. He picked it up and cleaned it with his glove. It was a key. Alex showed it to his dad. "We need to take this to the museum," his dad said. "I think it's made of silver."

Example.

Alex's dad was working in the yard in the ....winter........ .

1 Alex's dad asked Alex .... him in the yard.

2 Alex .... a computer game with his friends.

3 He .... a warm coat before he went outside.

4 There was something shining .... the flowers.

5 Alex's dad wanted to .... with the key.

2 Listening.

Listen and match.

Lily Oliver Dan Grace

Sam Charlie Alice

Chapter 6 Review

1 Reading and Writing.

Complete with the missing words.

TO: James

Dear James

I'm sending this email from our hotel ......in...... Spain. We're having an awful vacation. While we (1) .... traveling here, there was a bad storm. We (2) .... to wear life jackets on the ship. The waves were huge and it was very frightening. The hotel is terrible. We were eating dinner on the first night (3) .... my brother found a fly in his pasta. The weather is just (4) .... bad as the hotel. It's rained every day and there's (5) .... to do.

I can't wait to come home!

Emma

2 Listening.

Listen and write.

Museum of the Ocean

How much? Museum entry free for school children.

1 Go by: ....

2 Where is it? next to the ....

3 What are we going to see? a .... and old photos

4 What do we need to find out about? the sinking of the ....

5 Where does the bus return to? .... Street

Chapter 7 Review

1 Reading and Writing.

Read, find, and write the words.

Salt

One of the ....most.... important foods is salt. People and animals need some salt to help their bodies work (1) .... But did you know that a long time ago, salt was more expensive (2) .... meat? It was called "white gold." People used to (3) .... seawater to collect salt but it took a long time because they had to do it (4) .... Now salt is used in a lot of food because it makes it tasty. Even sweet foods like cookies have salt in them. But be careful! You shouldn't eat too (5) .... salt because that isn't good for you.

Example. most / more / as

1 good / well / better

2 than / that / then

3 fry / boil / roast

4 slowly / slow / slower

5 much / many / enough

2 Listening.

Listen and check ✓ the correct picture.

Example. What's George going to make?

a  ✓

b  ☐

c  ☐

1 What does George want from the store?

a  ☐

b  ☐

c  ☐

2 What time is Lily going to arrive?

a  ☐

b  ☐

c  ☐

3 Where should George put the clean pans?

a  ☐

b 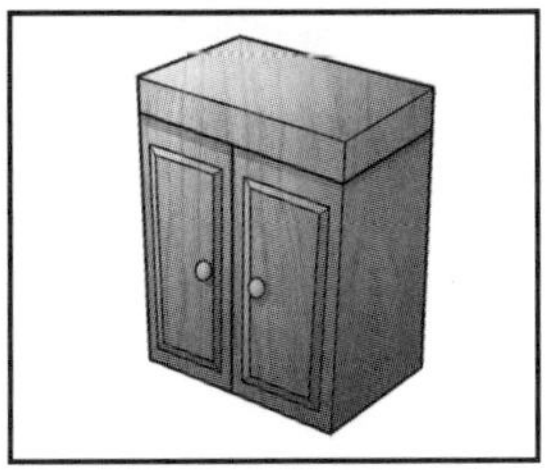 ☐

c  ☐

Chapter 8 Review

1 Reading and Writing.

Jessica and Adam are talking about Adam's vacation. What does Adam say? Write the letters.

Example.

Jessica: Hi, Adam. Did you enjoy your vacation in New York?

Adam: ....b....

1 **Jessica:** You're so lucky. Were you in a nice hotel?

Adam: ....

2 **Jessica:** What was the best thing about the vacation?

Adam: ....

3 **Jessica:** That sounds fantastic. Are you going to see them again?

Adam: ....

a I hope so. They told me they wanted to come and see me.

b Yes, thanks. I visited a lot of famous museums and I went to the theater. **(Example)**

c Yes, I stayed with a wonderful family downtown.

d No, my aunt said I could stay with her. She has an apartment there.

e I think it was the concert in Central Park. I made some new friends.

f No, I didn't have time to see everything.

2 Listening.

Listen and color, write, or draw.

Chapter 9 Review

1 Reading and Writing.

Read and write the words.

Example.

~~solar panels~~ a gift a village batteries a diary
wildlife wireless a city a watch news

Example.

These go on your house and turn sunlight into electricity. solar panels

1 A place in the country where people live.
It's smaller than a town. ______

2 You use this when you want to know what time it is. ______

3 This is something you give to another person. ______

4 These are used in electric items that you want to
use outside your house. ______

5 The creatures that live in the natural world. ______

2 Listening.

Where did Sam's friends stay on vacation? Listen and write the letters.

Charlie	c
George	
Daisy	
Anna	
Tom	
Lucy	

a 

b 

c 

d 

e 

f 

g 

h 

Chapter 1 Grammar

Lesson 2 simple past

My uncles	**used**	ink pens and chalkboards.	
They	**had to**	go to school very early.	
Did your friends	**go**	to the movie theater?	Yes they **did**.
			No they **didn't**.

1 **Circle the one that doesn't belong and write why.**

1 jump / take / brush / wash ....

2 do / run / ride / play ....

3 arrive / go / write / make ....

4 live / invite / perform / use ....

Think Again!
What's the difference between the verbs in A and B in the simple past?
A: dance, watch, ask, climb
B: go, have, see, wear

Lesson 5 *used to* + verb

My brothers	**used to**	like horror movies.	
They	**didn't use to**	play soccer every day.	
Did you	**use to**	have a pet?	Yes, we **did**.
			No, we **didn't**.

2 **Choose and write questions for a friend. Then ask and write their answers.**

have a dog? *play ping-pong?* *live in the U.S.?*
have cookies for breakfast? *go to bed early?* *like cartoons?*
have an imaginary friend? *sing in the shower?*

1 Did you use .... ? ....

2 Did you .... ? ....

3 .... ? ....

4 .... ? ....

Chapter 2 Grammar

Lesson 2 present perfect

How long **have** you	**studied** English?	**I've**	**studied** it	**for** five years.
		She's		**since** she was six.

1 Match.

1 How long have you
2 She's worked in an office
3 How long
4 He's played the drums since
5 How long have
6 We've played soccer for

a he was nine.
b have you studied art?
c done karate?
d two years.
e you been a firefighter?
f for eight years.

Lesson 5 *going to* & *might*

I'**m**/He'**s**/She'**s**	**going to**	**be** a doctor
I'**m not**/He **isn't**/She **isn't**	**going to**	
I/He/She	**might**	
	might not	
Are you	**going to**	travel?
Yes, **I am**. / No, **I'm not**. / **I might**.		

Think Again!

Definite plan or possible action?

I might go to the zoo.

2 Unscramble and write. Then draw: ☺ for a definite plan and 😐? for a possible action.

1 a / going / buy / scarf / . / to / She's

2 might / He / a / take / . / shower

3 No, / you / sing / ? / I'm / to / Are / not / . / going

4 him / . / I / said / see / might / tomorrow / I

Chapter 3 Grammar

Lesson 2 comparatives

The movie	**isn't as** good **as**	the book.
The carousel	**wasn't as** exciting **as**	the zip line.
English	**is just as** difficult **as**	math.
Scott's cake	**was just as** delicious **as**	Amy's cake.

Think Again!
Which adjectives have better and worse as their comparative forms?

1 Choose and write sentences comparing the things in pairs.

art & science kangaroos & sharks horror movies & animations
watching TV & playing soccer olives & bananas rowing & diving

1 ....
2 ....
3 ....
4 ....

Lesson 5 *-ed/-ing* adjectives

The horror movie was	**frightening.**	
My brother was	**frightened**	by the horror movie.

2 Circle.

My friend Billy went to a party at his uncle's house last week. He thought it would be 1 **boring** / **bored** so he took his video game to play. His mom was 2 **disappointing** / **disappointed** when she saw it. She told him to put it away and talk to his little cousins. Billy made up a great game to play with his cousins. But they weren't 3 **interesting** / **interested**. They didn't understand the game – it was 4 **confusing** / **confused**. So Billy hid under the table to play his video game again. His uncle found him there – Billy was really 5 **embarrassing** / **embarrassed**!

Chapter 4 Grammar

Lesson 2 present progressive

We're	playing	volleyball tomorrow.	
I'm not			
Are you	going	to Paris next year?	Yes, I am.
			No, I'm not.

1 Write about what your family is doing this weekend.

This weekend, ...

1 I'm ....

2 my mom ....

3 my dad ....

4 we ....

Lesson 5 words like *someone*

Is there	anything	in the cookie jar?
No, there's	nothing	there.
We're inviting	everyone	to the party.
Please ask	someone	to open the window.

Think Again!

What's wrong here?

There was no one in my bag.

2 Cross out the word that's wrong and write the correct word.

1 Have you packed ~~nothing~~ that you need for your trip? ......everything......

2 Would you like someone to eat? ....

3 Does anyone know the answer? No, everyone does. ....

4 Is no one in the classroom? Yes, someone is. ....

5 I'm bored. I have everything to do. ....

Chapter 5 Grammar

Lesson 2 be made of & be used for

What's the scarf	made of?	It's	made of	silk.
What's the box	used for?		used for	candy.

1 Complete the first two sentences. Then write sentences about three other things you have.

1 My bag is made of .... and it's used for ....

2 My shoes are .... and they're ....

3 .... and it's used for ....

4 ....

5 ....

Lesson 5 present passive

French	is spoken	in Canada.
Penguins	are found	in Antarctica.

2 Circle.

1 Lots of children **study** / **are studied by** Spanish.

2 The pizza **eats** / **is eaten by** my brother.

3 The cat **chases** / **is chased by** the mouse.

4 Fires **put out** / **are put out by** firefighters.

5 Plates **wash** / **are washed in** a dishwasher.

6 The thief **steals** / **is stolen by** the jewels.

Think Again!

Which verbs are used to make the passive?
What forms of the verbs?

Which is correct?
a Games have played at recess.
b Games are played at recess.
c Games are play at recess.

Chapter 6 Grammar

Lesson 2 past progressive & simple past

I	**was** sleep**ing**	when you **called**.
We	**were** play**ing** basketball	when you **arrived**.

1 Complete for you.

1 .... when I woke up.

2 I was reading when ....

3 .... my dad came home.

4 My friend was ....

5 I ....

6 We ....

Lesson 5 past progressive with *when/while*

While	I **was cooking**,	my brother **broke** a plate.
When	I **went** to the park,	you **were watching** a movie.
What	**were** you **doing**	**when** you **saw** the thief?

2 Use the clues to write sentences.

1 Paul / hide / when friends find him

Paul was hiding when his friends found him.

2 I / dance / when belt break

....

3 while Dad / walk to work / meet his friend

....

4 while we / build den / Jon climb the tree

....

5 what / you do / when see the shark?

....

Think Again!

What's wrong here? Why?

I watched TV when I was hearing a loud noise.

Chapter 7 Grammar

Lesson 2 adverbs

Can you do it	**quickly**?
Wash the tomatoes	**well.**

1 Write sentences using adverbs in the correct place.

1 slow – brush teeth I brush my teeth slowly.

2 careful – listen to teacher ....

3 quick – get out of bed ....

4 excited – celebrate festival ....

5 good – write stories ....

6 bad – sing ....

Lesson 5 *too much, too many & not enough*

Don't use	**too much**	salt.
I've eaten	**too many**	cookies
He didn't drink	**enough**	water.

Think Again!

Correct or not?

cookies too many

fruit too much

not enough water

2 Write about what you eat and drink.

1 I drink too much ....

2 I eat enough ....

3 .... too many ....

4 I don't eat enough ....

5 ....

6 ....

Chapter 8 Grammar

Lesson 2 reported speech

"I **have** a black dog," said Millie.	Millie said (that) she **had** a black dog.
"I **don't like** doing judo," Ben explained.	Ben explained (that) he **didn't like** doing judo.
"I **can do** it," said Ann.	Anne told me (that) she **could do** it.

1 **Complete with reported speech.**

1 Bobo the clown said *he had a red nose.*

2 He told us ....

3 He explained ....

4 He argued ....

5 He joked ....

Lesson 5 reported questions

"What **do you want** for lunch?" asked Mom.	Mom asked what **I wanted** for lunch.
"**Are you** OK?" asked Matt.	Matt asked if **I was** OK.

2 **You interview your favorite sports star. Tell a friend what you asked him/her.**

• Are you excited about the Olympics? • How many competitions have you won? • When do you train? • Do you want to try a different sport?

1 I asked him/her ....

2 Then I asked if ....

3 Next I asked ....

4 Finally, ...

Think Again!

Laura asked Sam if he could skate. How did Sam answer Laura?

"Yes, I can."

"For two years."

Chapter 9 Grammar

Lesson 2 *will/won't*

In the future,	we'll **live**	underground.
	we **won't need**	money.

1 Write about you, using *will* or *won't* + the correct verb.

When I grow up, …

1 I .... a police officer.

2 I .... a lot of pets.

3 I .... in an apartment.

4 I .... to Australia.

5 I .... with dolphins.

6 I .... tennis.

Lesson 5 questions with *will*

Will we	**have** keys to get into our houses?	Yes, we **will**.
		No, we **won't**.
How **will** we	**travel**?	We'll **use** flying cars.

2 Write questions about a friend's birthday party.

1 What will .... ?

2 Where will .... ?

3 How .... ?

4 Who .... ?

5 Will .... ?

Think Again!

Which is correct?

Yes, I'll. / Yes, I will.

No, there won't be. / No, there won't.